Unit 1

Using Numbers

D1308721

Unit Overview

The purpose of this unit is to give students a general sense of the size of numbers and the relationships among them. Students will become familiar with counting, estimating, rounding, and grouping numbers. This will lay the foundation for other units.

Everyday Numbers page 13

Have students fill in the Personal Survey individually. Then go through the survey as a group and discuss the following questions: *"Which numbers do you know for sure? Which did you have to estimate (guess at)? For which numbers is it critical that you have an exact answer? Why?"* Be sure to show that different answers are acceptable as long as students can support their ideas.

Talk About It page 13

After students have assigned categories to the Personal Survey questions, have them compare their assignments with a partner. If answers are different, explore the following questions: *"Is either answer wrong? Why or why not?"* You may use this opportunity to discuss, *"Is there* always *one right answer when you work with numbers?"* Ask for examples of problems that have only one correct answer and problems that have more than one.

Working Together page 43

Have students analyze why they chose a particular activity from the chart. Did they choose it because it burns the most calories? because they like the activity? a combination of the two? Use their responses to discuss how numbers can be one of many factors used when making a decision. Have students work in pairs to brainstorm a list of decisions that use a combination of numbers and other factors.

Activity Overview

To find general information about *Math Sense*, including scope and sequence charts, see www.math-sense.com.

Student Book Lesson	Pages in SB	TRG	Activity Type	PCM Number
Success in Math	14	4	Communication	
Counting and Grouping	16	4	Reasoning/Hands-On	
The Number Line	18	4	Cooperative Learning	
Place Value	20	5	Hands-On	1, 2
Rounding	22	5	Number Sense	
Does the Answer Make Sense?	24	6	Real-Life Application	3
Gridding in Answers	26	6	Grid Activity	4
Calendars	30	7	Hands-On	5
Using Dollars and Cents	32	7	Communication	
Paying with Cash	34	8	Hands-On/Role-Playing	2
Checks and Money Orders	36	8	Hands-On	6
What Time Is It?	38	9	Real-Life Application	7
Tables and Schedules	40	9	Real-Life Application	8

Success in Math

SB p. 14

Lesson Objectives

- explore one's feelings about math
- get some positive ideas about math and one's own math abilities

Activity
Thinking About Math

Purpose: reinforce the ideas in the lesson

What to Do

Have students write one question about each of these topics: (1) a negative experience with math, (2) a positive experience with math, and (3) a goal for learning math. You should model each type of question for the students. Write these questions on the board or overhead projector: "What is your worst experience with learning math? When have you used math to solve a problem? What do you think you will accomplish if you get better at math?" Have students share their questions with a partner. The partners should write responses and discuss them.

What to Look For

You can use the responses to get to know each student better and to get a sense of individual experiences and goals. Go around to each pair and read or listen to the responses. Give some personal math anecdotes of your own so students become more comfortable with you.

Counting and Grouping

SB p. 16

Lesson Objectives

- understand basic counting and how grouping helps counting
- get an overview of different methods of grouping, including patterns, evens and odds, tallies, and place values

Activity
Grouping Strategies

Purpose: reinforce the ideas in the lesson

Materials

- lots of small objects, such as paper clips or coins

What to Do

1. Discuss the tally chart on student book page 16. Ask, *"How did you find the totals for each column? What is the advantage of counting by fives rather than by ones? How else can we group numbers or objects to make them easier to count?"*

2. Have pairs or small groups of students work with 30 or more real objects (paper clips, coins, etc.). Have them devise ways of grouping that make the objects easier to count: twos, fives, tens, etc. Discuss whether they are grouping by even or odd numbers to reinforce "Making Connections: Odd and Even Numbers" on student book page 17.

The Number Line
Tools

SB p. 18

Lesson Objectives

- become familiar with the concept of the number line for comparing and ordering numbers
- become familiar with the comparison symbols
- relate the number line to real-life objects

Common Difficulties

Number lines and comparison symbols are abstract concepts. This activity lets you introduce them in concrete ways. If students need additional reinforcement using symbols, make up other problems like 8–15 on student book page 19.

Activity
Real-Life Number Lines

Purpose: introduce the ideas in the lesson

MATH SENSE

Skills, Problem Solving, Tools, and Applications

TEACHER'S RESOURCE GUIDE
Whole Numbers and Money

Jan Phillips

Acknowledgments

Advisers

Connie Eichhorn, Supervisor of Transitional Services
Omaha Public Schools Omaha, NE

Lois Kasper, Instructional Facilitator
Board of Education of the City of New York New York, NY

Jan Phillips, Assistant Professor
William Rainey Harper College Palatine, IL

Mary B. Puleo, Assistant Director
Sarasota County Adult and Community Education Sarasota, FL

Margaret Rogers, Coordinator
San Juan Unified Adult Education Sacramento, CA

New Readers Press

Contents

Math Sense: Whole Numbers and Money
Teacher's Resource Guide
ISBN 1-56420-384-0
Copyright © 2003, 1995 New Readers Press
New Readers Press
Division of ProLiteracy Worldwide
1320 Jamesville Avenue, Syracuse, New York 13210
www.newreaderspress.com

Printed in the United States of America
9 8 7 6 5 4 3 2 1

All proceeds from the sale of New Readers Press materials
support literacy programs in the United States and worldwide.

Developer: Learning Unlimited, Oak Park, IL
Content Editing: Sybil M. Sosin Publishing Services
Series Editor: Judi Lauber
Production Director: Heather Witt
Illustrations: Linda Tiff, James P. Wallace
Cover Design: Kimbrly Koennecke

Casio *fx*-260 image courtesy of Casio, Inc.

Materials

- a yardstick
- a thermometer
- a scale

What to Do

1. Have students write questions about *greater than* and *less than* using the yardstick, thermometer, and scale. They will then use comparison symbols to answer the questions. Model these questions and answers first:
   - Which is smaller, 3 pounds or 15 pounds?
     3 pounds $<$ 15 pounds
   - Compare 1 foot to 12 inches.
     1 foot $=$ 12 inches
   - Which is higher, a Fahrenheit temperature of 47 degrees or 13 degrees?
     47 degrees $>$ 13 degrees

2. Pair off students and have them swap and answer each other's questions.

3. Then have them discuss the symbols they used.

Place Value

SB p. 20

Lesson Objective

- gain a concrete understanding of place values

Common Difficulties

Many students don't understand place value. For instance, they don't know that 80 is 8 tens or that 300 is 3 groups of 100. The following activity builds that understanding with real-life materials.

Activity
Building Numbers

Purpose: extend the ideas in the lesson

Materials

- PCM 1: Thousands Place Value Chart, p. 42
- PCM 2: Bills and Coins, p. 43, or play money

What to Do

1. Practice talking about numbers in expanded form. For example, 637 is 6 hundreds, 3 tens, and 7 ones.

2. Distribute a copy of PCM 1 and ones, tens, and hundreds from PCM 2 to each student.

3. Tell students an amount such as $578 and have them place bills on their chart to show it. They should use the smallest number of bills possible. For $578 they would have 5 hundreds, 7 tens, and 8 ones.

4. Pick up a $1 bill and have students "add 1" and read the new amount, $579, as money and in expanded form (5 hundreds, 7 tens, and 9 ones). "Add 1" again and discuss how the number becomes $580. Ask students if they are still using the smallest number of bills possible. Encourage students to replace the bills in the ones place. Did they use one $10 bill? You also can "add 10" to numbers and discuss what happens. Repeat with other numbers between 1 and 999.

Variation: Have students put money on the chart and exchange charts with a partner. The partner should read and write the amount of money.

What to Look For

Without being told so, students are regrouping ones to tens, tens to hundreds, and hundreds to thousands. After they have been doing this for some time, introduce the term *regrouping* and mention that they will be using this throughout this book. You may use this activity again when students begin regrouping in addition and subtraction.

Rounding

SB p. 22

Lesson Objectives

- choose appropriate rounded values for numbers
- begin to develop the ability to estimate

Visualizing Rounded Numbers

Purpose: reinforce the ideas in the lesson

Materials

- self-stick removable notes

What to Do

1. Draw a large number line on the blackboard. Label the units by tens, up to 100. Give each student about five small self-stick notes and ask them to write a number between 0 and 100 on one of them.

2. Then have each student stick his or her number on the blackboard above the multiple of 10 nearest the number, as in the following example. Discuss students' choices.

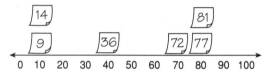

3. Remove the self-stick notes and change the units to hundreds. Have students write any number from 0 to 1,000 on a self-stick note and place it on the board above the nearest 100.

4. Continue this activity by changing the units again. Ask students to defend the placement of their numbers on the number line. Be sure they can explain their choices. Relate rounded numbers to real life by asking a question such as, *"Do you think there are exactly two hundred eighty million people in the United States?"*

Does the Answer Make Sense?
Problem Solver

SB p. 24

Lesson Objective

- develop the ability to judge the reasonableness of answers to math problems

Common Difficulties

Students often accept any number resulting from a calculation. Problem solving is complete only when students ask themselves, "Is my answer sensible? Does my answer fit the situation?"

Relating Numbers to Real Life

Purpose: extend the ideas in the lesson

Materials

- PCM 3: Whole Numbers from 0 to 100, p. 44
- overhead transparency of PCM 3 and marker

What to Do

1. Have students work in pairs. Distribute a copy of PCM 3 to each pair. Ask students to label the numbers with something in real life. For example, "24 cans in a case" or "24 hours in a day." Give them about five minutes to work in pairs, labeling as many numbers as they can.

2. Record the answers on an overhead transparency of PCM 3. Be sure the students explain their answers. Discuss units. For example, *"How is twenty-four hours different in units from twenty-four cans in a case of soda?"* (Even though there are 24 of both items, the units cause the number to represent different things. Twenty-four hours can be broken down into minutes or seconds, while 24 cans of soda can be broken down into 6-packs or ounces.)

Gridding in Answers
Tools

SB p. 26

Lesson Objectives

- fill in whole numbers on a five-column grid
- understand place value

Deal a Number

Purpose: reinforce the ideas in the lesson

Materials

- PCM 4: Five-Column Grids, p. 45
- deck of playing cards with face cards and aces removed

What to Do

Distribute a copy of PCM 4 to each student. Explain that students will take turns forming a number using randomly drawn cards.

Have a student come to the front of the class and shuffle the cards. Then assign the student a place value target of either hundreds, thousands, or ten thousands. The student will deal enough cards to create the number: three cards for hundreds, four for thousands, and five for ten thousands. Then the student will turn over the cards and read the number to the class. Have students fill in the number on one of the grids on PCM 4.

Students should take turns until enough numbers are created to fill all of the grids.

What to Look For

This activity will reinforce the correct order of place value columns and the meaning of digits. Make sure students record the number at the top of the grid before they fill in the grid circles.

Calendars
Application

SB p. 30

Lesson Objectives

- read and understand the organization of a calendar
- write dates using words and numbers

Activity
Using a Calendar

Purpose: extend the ideas in the lesson

Materials

- PCM 5: Calendar Instructions, p. 46
- a current year calendar for each student
- pencils, pens, and highlighters

What to Do

1. Distribute a calendar and a copy of PCM 5 to each student. Tell students to follow the instructions on PCM 5. Allow them about five minutes to work individually. (*Note:* for number 11 and student book page 31, if "today's date" is in May, June, or July, there will be only two different ways to write it.)

2. Have students compare calendars with a partner. Move around the room commenting on and questioning similarities and differences that you observe.

Using Dollars and Cents

SB p. 32

Lesson Objectives

- read, write, and say dollar and cent amounts
- select bills and coins to represent an amount of money

Activity
Writing Money Amounts

Purpose: reinforce the ideas in the lesson

Materials

- blank overhead transparency and marker

What to Do

Go around the class having each student say a money amount. Suggest amounts by asking questions like, *"How much would you spend on a new car? What is the price of your favorite candy bar? What is the cost of a gallon of gasoline? What is the minimum wage?"*

Students should write all the amounts listed on a piece of paper using dollar or cent symbols, while you record the amounts on a blank overhead transparency. Allow students time to compare answers. Then show the overhead transparency and have students check their answers.

What to Look For

Watch out for the zeros. For instance, discuss the difference between $18.50 and $18.05. Point out that $12 is the same as $12.00. Some students confuse commas and decimal points. Use large amounts, such as $18,056.75, to show both symbols.

Paying with Cash
Problem Solver

SB p. 34

Lesson Objectives

- select bills and coins to pay for items and to return change
- estimate money amounts

Activity
Money Transactions

Purpose: reinforce the ideas in the lesson

Materials

- PCM 2: Bills and Coins, p. 43
- advertising flyers from newspapers

What to Do

1. Have students work in groups of three or four. Distribute flyers and $200 worth of bills and coins from PCM 2 to each group. A reasonable selection of each currency should be included.

2. Within each group, assign roles of buyer, merchant, and bookkeeper.

   The buyer

   - has a budget of $200
   - makes three purchases from the flyers
   - pays for the first purchase using the exact amount of bills and coins
   - pays for the second purchase by rounding up to the nearest $10
   - pays for the third purchase with a reasonable amount of money

The merchant

- checks the amount paid
- counts out the appropriate change as described in the lesson

The bookkeeper

- records the transactions under three columns, headed *Price, Amount Paid,* and *Amount of Change*

What to Look For

Circulate among the groups to make sure that a variety of amounts are being spent. Ask questions such as, *"Is there another way to make change for that item? Did you use the smallest number of bills and coins possible? How did you estimate which bills and coins to use?"*

Have students switch roles and repeat the process if time allows.

Checks and Money Orders
Application

SB p. 36

Lesson Objectives

- understand the parts of a check and a money order
- practice writing checks and money orders

Common Difficulties

Students may be apprehensive about writing a check. You will need to discuss some examples of completed checks before they write their own. Spelling will also be a concern. Emphasize the importance of writing the correct amount. For example, write $358.00 and $3,580.00 on the board. Ask, *"Are these amounts the same?"*

Activity
Writing Checks and Money Orders

Purpose: reinforce the ideas in the lesson

Materials

- PCM 6: Checks and Money Orders, p. 47
- receipts and bills (grocery receipts, copies of doctor bills, electric bills, etc.)

What to Do

Distribute bills, receipts, and a copy of PCM 6 to each student. Discuss how students pay their bills. Have each student pay three bills using the checks and money order on PCM 6. After they finish, have them exchange PCMs with a partner to discuss any questions or make corrections. Go over any questions or comments with the group.

What Time Is It?
Tools

SB p. 38

Lesson Objectives

* read analog and digital clocks
* practice writing digital times

Activity
Time on My Hands

Purpose: extend the ideas in the lesson

Materials

* PCM 7: Clocks, p. 48
* overhead transparency of PCM 7 and marker

What to Do

Model on the overhead transparency how you schedule your day. For example:

I get up at 6:45 A.M.   I catch the bus at 7:30 A.M.

Distribute a copy of PCM 7 to each student. Ask students to record their daily schedules by marking times on the clocks and labeling them with their activities. Encourage students to think about elapsed time, such as how much time it takes to get to work or the amount of time the class takes. Ask questions such as, *"Do you wear a watch? How many clocks do you have at home? Are they all set at the same time? How long do you take for routine activities like sleeping, eating, dressing, watching TV, etc.?"*

Tables and Schedules
Tools

SB p. 40

Lesson Objectives

* practice reading tables and schedules
* distinguish between rows and columns

Activity
Reading a Tax Table

Purpose: extend the ideas in the lesson

Materials

* PCM 8: Tax Table, p. 49
* overhead transparency of PCM 8

What to Do

1. If possible, obtain a current 1040A tax booklet from a library or a post office. This will aid discussion and help you answer questions. Because taxes affect everyone, there will be a lot of interest in this topic. Ask questions such as, *"On what day are taxes due each year? What is the difference between federal and state income tax? Who pays taxes? What are deductions?"*

2. Distribute copies of PCM 8. Put the overhead transparency of PCM 8 on an overhead projector. Discuss what the column and row headings mean. Make sure students can read the table. Have each student write an amount of taxable income for an imaginary person (within the boundaries of the table) and exchange amounts with a partner. Ask the partner to decide if the person is single, married, etc. Then they can find the amount of tax the person owes.

3. As a group, discuss the answers. Ask, *"What does the government do with this money?"* (Possible responses: The government spends it on national defense, veterans benefits, foreign affairs, social programs, law enforcement, education, general government costs, interest on the national debt, etc.)

Unit 2 Addition

Unit Overview

The purpose of this unit is to develop a solid foundation of addition skills. Students will build upon the addition facts by using an addition table, the number line, and calculators. They will extend their skills and apply them to everyday situations. Estimation, problem-solving strategies, and working with money will help students successfully use addition skills.

When Do I Add? page 45

Ask students to help you make a list of words that mean addition. Put the list on the board as they say words such as *total, plus,* and *add.* Give students a few minutes to write sentences describing when they might add at home, at school, at the store, and at work. Encourage them to use words from the list.

Talk About It page 45

Because we can only combine things that are alike, we often have to rename the units of items. For instance, ask students to think of as many ways as possible to rename a dollar. Some examples are 4 quarters, 10 dimes, etc. Ask them to rename a year. Examples are 12 months, 52 weeks, and so on. This will review measurement units discussed in unit 1.

Working Together page 73

As students work together developing their budgets, move around the class asking questions such as, *"What miscellaneous expenses can you expect? Why did you decide to save that amount of money? How much can you save in a year at that rate? Do you have enough information about the real cost of transportation to make an informed decision?"* Stress the need to make choices.

After the pairs complete the budget, ask the whole group to discuss how addition helped them make decisions. Ask, *"What other skills did you use to make decisions?"* Answers may include past experiences and checking prices.

Activity Overview

To find general information about *Math Sense*, including scope and sequence charts, see www.math-sense.com.

Student Book Lesson	Pages in SB	TRG	Activity Type	PCM Number
Building an Addition Table	46	11	Investigating Patterns	9
Addition Facts	48	11	Skill Building	10
Addition Strategies	50	12	Communication	
Adding Larger Numbers	52	12	Estimation/Hands-On	2, 11
Adding with Regrouping	54	13	Hands-On	12
Finding Perimeter	56	13	Cooperative Learning	13
Adding Thousands	60	14	Math for Fun	
Understanding Word Problems	62	14	Reasoning/Communication	14
Adding on a Calculator	64	15	Hands-On	
Adding Dollars and Cents	66	15	Problem Solving/Calculator	15
Estimating Costs	68	16	Real World/Role-Playing	
Gridding in Money Answers	70	16	Grid Activity	4, 16

Building an Addition Table

SB p. 46

Lesson Objectives

- use an addition table to identify addition facts
- explore patterns in addition
- learn the commutative property of addition

Activity

Building an Addition Table

Purpose: identify patterns

Materials

- PCM 9: Grid, p. 50

What to Do

1. Distribute a copy of PCM 9 to each student. Let students work in pairs as they each follow the instructions on student book page 46 to create an addition table. Discuss how to use the table.

2. Discuss part B on student book page 46. Ask the students to show other examples of the commutative property. Let students use the table to do parts C, D, and E.

3. Have students work with a partner to identify number patterns from the table. For example:
   - when you add a number to itself, the answer is even: $3 + 3 = 6$
   - when you add one number to the next consecutive number, the answer is odd: $3 + 4 = 7$
   - when you add numbers in any order, the answer is the same: $5 + 8 = 13$ and $8 + 5 = 13$
   - when you add zero to a number, the answer is that number: $9 + 0 = 9$

   This exploration should lead directly to "Addition Facts" on student book page 48.

Expansion/Reinforcement: Students can fill in the remaining columns and rows on their addition tables.

Addition Facts

SB p. 48

Lesson Objectives

- picture addition on the number line
- memorize and practice the addition facts

Common Difficulties

If students have trouble picturing addition on a number line, distribute rulers and ask them to measure in inches. To picture $4 + 5 = 9$, have them draw a line 4 inches long. Then have them continue the line for 5 more inches and measure the result. The line should be 9 inches long. Continue with more examples.

Activity

One-Minute Speed Drills

Purpose: reinforce the ideas in the lesson

Materials

- PCM 10: Addition Speed Drills, p. 51
- timer

What to Do

Use the speed drills one at a time as a class warm-up. This should encourage students to memorize the basic addition facts.

Distribute copies of PCM 10 facedown. Allow students one minute to complete the assigned drill. Let students check their own drill as you read the correct answers. (*Note:* Fill in the answers on your own copy of PCM 10 to create an answer key.)

Each drill is harder than the previous one. Use your best judgment about how often to administer the drills and whether to repeat any of them. Students should save their unanswered drills for future class use.

Addition Strategies
Problem Solver

SB p. 50

Lesson Objectives

- use combinations of 10 to aid addition skills
- write and solve addition equations
- become familiar with variables

Activity
Mystery Numbers

Purpose: extend the ideas in the lesson

What to Do

1. Model writing equations. Say to students, *"I'm thinking of a mystery number. When you add seven and eight, you get this number. What is it?"* Write on the board: $7 + 8 = M$.

2. Then say, *"This equation asks the same question. What is the mystery number M?"* Write $15 = M$.

3. Say to students, *"Use the addition facts to guess the mystery number that you add to nine to get twelve."* Write the equation $T + 9 = 12$. *"What is the number?"* Write $T = 3$. Then say, *"If a board is laid end to end with another board of the same length, and their total length is eighteen feet, how long is each board?"* Write the equation $b + b = 18$ and ask students to solve it. Write $b = 9$.

4. Discuss how these equations communicate the same ideas as the spoken sentences. Have each student write a mystery sentence that uses addition. Have students exchange their sentence with a partner who will write an equation for the sentence. Emphasize that different variables can be used. Let students present their equations to the class. Have the class find the solutions to the equations.

Adding Larger Numbers

SB p. 52

Lesson Objectives

- add larger numbers by lining up like place values
- use estimation to approximate an answer and to check if the exact answer makes sense

Activity
Knowing Right from Wrong

Purpose: reinforce the ideas in the lesson

Materials

- PCM 2: Bills and Coins, p. 43
- PCM 11: Adding Large Numbers, p. 52

What to Do

1. Model the correct way to line up an addition problem. Emphasize the importance of lining up digits that have the same place value. Then demonstrate using estimation and money to show that the answer makes sense.

   Example: $327 + $42 = $747

Estimate	Correction		Money	
$330	$327	100	10	1
+ 40	+ 42	100	10	1
$370	$369	100	10	1
			10	1
			10	1
			10	1
				1
				1
				1

   $$300 + 60 + 9 = \$369$$

   Error

   $327
   + 42
   _____
   $747

2. Ask students to work with a partner. Give each pair sufficient bills from PCM 2. Distribute a copy of PCM 11 to each student and review the

instructions. When students have completed the PCM, ask for volunteers to demonstrate each problem.

3. Then ask students to show that the incorrect answers were caused by incorrectly lining up the problems.

Adding with Regrouping

SB p. 54

Lesson Objectives

- become familiar with regrouping in addition
- use information from a map

Common Difficulties

Students need concrete experiences to reinforce the abstract idea of regrouping. They need to learn that when the sum of the digits in a particular place value is 10 or more, they must regroup to the next highest place value. This is because, in a base ten system, the highest digit is 9.

Activity
Regrouping in Addition

Purpose: reinforce the ideas in the lesson

Materials

- PCM 12: Regrouping Chart, p. 53
- overhead transparency of PCM 12 and marker

What to Do

On an overhead transparency of PCM 12, model regrouping in addition using $356 + 36 = 392$.

Add	Thousands	Hundreds	Tens	Ones
1			X	
356 + 36 392		X X X	X X X X X X X X	X X X X X X X X X X X X
			3	9	2

Operation / Regroup →

1. Place the correct number of counters (X's) in each place value to represent 356 and 36.

2. Total the ones column. Regroup 10 of the 12 counters to the tens place value.

3. Continue totaling columns from right to left until all columns are totaled. Regroup whenever 10 counters accumulate.

4. Demonstrate regrouping with the addition equation in the far left column of the regrouping chart shown here. Emphasize that writing the regrouped amount helps to ensure accuracy.

5. Ask students to put into their own words what happened in the problem. Give them time to ask questions.

Distribute copies of PCM 12 to all students. Have them work in groups of three or four on addition problems. Ask each student to demonstrate one problem to their group. Suggested problems are:

325	6,417	1,749
+ 591	+ 373	+ 31
(916)	(6,790)	(1,780)

286	2,048	1,465
+ 704	+ 733	+ 2,005
(990)	(2,781)	(3,470)

Students may ask about regrouping more than once in the same problem. Encourage them to explore how repeated regrouping works. For example, 10 ones equal 1 ten, 10 tens equal 1 hundred, etc.

Finding Perimeter
Application

SB p. 56

Lesson Objectives

- recognize a square, rectangle, and triangle
- measure length in English and metric units
- find the perimeter of a square, rectangle, and triangle

Activity
Measuring Perimeter

Purpose: extend the ideas in the lesson

Materials

- PCM 13: Leonardo da Vinci, p. 54
- rulers, yardsticks, tape measures
- objects that can be measured: wallet photo, notebook paper, index cards, floor mat, a border or frame

What to Do

1. Begin a discussion about measuring with rulers (English and metric), yardsticks, or tape measures. Draw lines on the board and ask students to measure them to the nearest whole unit that you specify. Ask questions such as, *"How do you know whether to use a ruler, yardstick, or tape measure? When do you give your answers in inches or feet?"* Extend this idea to regrouping 12 inches to 1 foot, or 3 feet to 1 yard.

2. Distribute a copy of PCM 13 to each student. To practice measuring length and width, use the Leonardo da Vinci activity. In groups of three or four, have students complete the activity, then discuss their results.

3. Have students find the perimeter of objects in the classroom such as photos, paper, index cards, or frames around the blackboard or a window. Ask questions such as, *"Do you need to measure all four sides of a square? When would you need to measure perimeter in real life? Can you accurately estimate the perimeter of an object just by looking at it?"*

Adding Thousands

SB p. 60

Lesson Objectives

- extend addition skills by adding larger numbers
- practice regrouping more than once in addition

Common Difficulties

When three or more large numbers are added, the regrouping may total 20 or more. Point out to students that writing the regrouped amount in the next column helps keep track of amounts (for example, a

2 for 2 tens). Too often, students sacrifice accuracy for speed. Use the regrouping chart (PCM 12) and the activity "Making Connections: Maps and Distances" on student book page 55 to show regrouping more than once.

Activity
Addition Cross Number Puzzle

Purpose: extend the ideas in the lesson

What to Do

Give students time to fill in the cross number puzzle on student book page 61. Upon completion, review the answers as a class. Guide discussion about the problems in the puzzle. Ask, *"Which problems were the easiest? Could you do any of them in your head? What did you have to watch out for? Did you see any patterns?"* Point out a pattern such as $9 + 9 = 18$ and $29 + 9 = 38$.

Draw the following portion of the puzzle on the board. Reinforce place value by asking, *"What value does the seven have in one hundred seventy-nine? What values do the sevens have in seven hundred seven?"*

Understanding Word Problems
Problem Solver

SB p. 62

Lesson Objectives

- develop the sense that word problems come from real-life situations
- identify the question being asked in a word problem
- use problem-solving strategies

Common Difficulties

Some vocabulary terms used in word problems can be difficult. Students should be encouraged to use resources such as the glossary at the back of their book. Knowing where to start the problem-solving process may also be confusing. Emphasize underlining the question as a first step. For problem 3 in the student book, make sure students understand that to double the recipe, they add the given amounts twice.

Activity
Understanding Word Problems

Purpose: reinforce the ideas in the lesson

Materials
- PCM 14: Understanding Word Problems, p. 55

What to Do
Have students work in groups of three. Distribute a copy of PCM 14 to each student. Each group should do all of the problems. Upon completion, have each group explain to the class how they solved one of the problems. Ask them questions such as, *"Did you identify the question first? What strategies did you use to solve the problem?"*

Adding on a Calculator
Tools

SB p. 64

Lesson Objectives
- become familiar with using a calculator
- practice adding on a calculator

Activity
Adding on the Calculator

Purpose: reinforce the ideas in the lesson

Materials
- calculators

What to Do
1. Ask students to write four addition problems on a sheet of paper. Ask them to use numbers in the thousands. At least two of the problems should add three or more numbers.

2. Have each student pass his or her paper to the student on his or her right. Have students write an estimate next to each problem they receive.

3. Students should pass the papers to the right again. The next person should use a calculator to find the exact answers and write them on the paper.

4. Students then return the papers to the original problem-writers, who should check the estimates and answers using a calculator.

5. Discuss the results of this activity. Make sure students feel comfortable using a calculator. Help them when they have questions. If you feel it would be beneficial, repeat the procedure.

What to Look For
Tell students that if the answer to a problem has too many digits for the display area of the calculator, it will not be accurate. The calculator may give an error symbol or change the answer into scientific notation. For instance, a display of 1.1244 08 means 112,440,000 but may be a rounded number. Have them test this on their calculators by adding numbers in the 10 millions.

Using the Casio *fx*-260 for the GED
When using a scientific calculator, students should reset the display by pressing $\boxed{\text{ON}}$ or $\boxed{\text{AC}}$ before each new calculation. On the Casio calculator, the equal key is located directly below the addition key. If students are used to a calculator with the equal key in the lower right corner, they may hit the $\boxed{\text{M+}}$ key in error. You may want to refer students to an image of the Casio *fx*-260 calculator on student book page 222.

Adding Dollars and Cents

SB p. 66

Lesson Objectives
- add money amounts by lining up like place values
- practice adding money amounts on a calculator

Common Difficulties
If an amount is given as $25, students often forget that it can be written as $25.00. Explain that the two

zeros mean there are no cents. For practice, have students record money amounts as you say them.

Activity
Check Your Resources

Purpose: extend the ideas in the lesson

Materials:

- PCM 15: Checking Your Resources, p. 56
- calculators

What to Do

Model the activity for the class. Add a column of amounts such as $5, $3.25, and $.78. Check your answer on a calculator. State whether the total is less than, greater than, or equal to a given amount, such as $10. In this case, $9.03 < $10.

Distribute copies of PCM 15 to all students. Ask them to follow the instructions and check their work with calculators. Upon completion, discuss the problems and compare answers. Ask students in what situations they might use calculators to add money.

Estimating Costs
Application

SB p. 68

Lesson Objectives

- apply addition skills to real-life situations
- estimate costs

Activity
The Garage Sale

Purpose: extend the ideas in the lesson

Materials

- brown paper grocery bags
- markers
- calculators

What to Do

Each student will need a paper bag, a calculator, and a marker. Begin a class discussion about garage sales. Ask, *"Have you ever shopped at a garage sale? Have you ever had a garage sale? What kind of items might be sold there? How do people decide what price an item should be? How do you negotiate a price?"*

1. Tell students the following: *"On your bag, list ten items from home that you would sell at a garage sale. Write an estimated value on the bag next to each item."*

2. Split the class into two groups, "buyers" and "sellers." Lay out the sellers' bags for all of the buyers to see. Each buyer is allowed to spend up to $50 (or $100 depending on the prices of items). Buyers should see how close they can get to that amount. Buyers and sellers may negotiate prices and use calculators when necessary.

3. Ask buyers to use the reverse side of their bags to keep a list of their purchases under these headings: *Item, Price Asked,* and *Price Paid.*

4. The sellers should try to make the best deals possible and record the amount they accepted next to each item sold. After 5 or 10 minutes, reverse the roles. Ask students to total their purchases and sales. Discuss the "good" deals, how calculators were used, and whether estimating was useful.

Gridding in Money Answers
Tools

SB p. 70

Lesson Objectives

- fill in money amounts as decimals on a five-column grid
- add amounts of money

Activity
Price Tags

Purpose: reinforce the ideas in the lesson

Materials

- PCM 4: Five-Column Grids, p. 45
- PCM 16: Price Tags, p. 57
- catalogs, newspaper ads, grocery circulars (one per pair of students)

What to Do

Have students work in pairs. Distribute a copy of PCM 16 to each pair, and have them choose nine items and find their regular or sale prices. (No item should have a regular price greater than $500.) Have students record the items and prices on the price tags on PCM 16.

Have students cut apart the price tags. Collect all price tags and place them in a box or bowl so that they can be easily drawn out.

Distribute a copy of PCM 4 to each student. Invite a student to draw out two or three price tags. Have the student read the items and the prices to the class. Have students work individually to find the total of the items and record it in one of the grids on PCM 4.

Continue until all grids are used.

What to Look For

Make sure students place the decimal point in its own column. Encourage students to use estimation to make sure their answers make sense. Save the price tags to create addition and subtraction problems in the future.

Unit 3 Subtraction

Unit Overview

The purpose of this unit is to develop fundamental subtraction skills. Students will use their understanding of the addition facts to learn the subtraction facts. The number line and calculators will help them develop ability in using the subtraction operation. Strategies for recognizing and solving subtraction problems will also be explored. Working with money and using calculators will provide experience with real-life applications.

When Do I Subtract? page 75

As a class, discuss the two main uses for the subtraction operation given on page 74. Ask which words from the list on page 75 refer to use #1 or use #2. Can students think of other words or phrases that compare numbers? Ask students to give real-life examples of when they might use subtraction. Let them know that they'll be learning strategies to help them improve their subtraction skills.

Talk About It page 75

Bring in newspaper advertisements to compare cars and prices. Ask students what they consider important when selecting a car. They might say gas mileage, price, age of car, four-wheel drive, color, etc. Which comparisons might involve subtraction? Ask students how they might use subtraction even after they have decided which car to purchase. For instance, they would want to know how much money they owe after making a $500 deposit, or how many months are left on the warranty, and so on.

Working Together page 105

Break the class into pairs to investigate these problems. Assign one problem to each pair. Allow time to discuss and explore. Then let each pair present the results of their investigations to the whole class. Encourage students to use math vocabulary and to be as specific as possible. Commend their good work.

Activity Overview

To find general information about *Math Sense*, including scope and sequence charts, see www.math-sense.com.

Student Book Lesson	Pages in SB	TRG	Activity Type	PCM Number
Subtraction Strategies	76	19	Investigating Patterns	9
Subtraction Facts	78	19	Skill Building	17
Subtracting Larger Numbers	80	19	Demonstration	18
Deciding to Add or Subtract	82	20	Cooperative Learning	
Subtracting by Regrouping	84	20	Hands-On	12
Regrouping More than Once	88	21	Investigation	12, 19
What Do I Need to Find?	90	21	Reasoning/Writing	20
Subtracting from Zeros	92	22	Real-Life Application	21, 22
Subtracting Dollars and Cents	94	22	Real-Life Application	
Understanding Your Paycheck	96	22	Hands-On	
Subtracting on a Calculator	98	23	Hands-On	
Figuring Change	100	23	Hands-On	2
Gridding in Answers	102	24	Grid Activity	4

Subtraction Strategies
Problem Solver

SB p. 76

Lesson Objectives

- relate subtraction to addition facts
- picture subtraction on the number line

Activity
Addition and Subtraction Relationship

Purpose: reinforce the ideas in the lesson

Materials

- overhead transparency of PCM 9, p. 50

What to Do

Put the overhead transparency of a filled-in addition table on the overhead projector. Tell the students that you have the answers and that they are going to write the problems. Example: *"The answer is six. What's the addition problem?"*

3 + 3	5 + 1
4 + 2	6 + 0

"What are the related subtraction problems?"

$$6 - 3 = 3 \qquad 6 - 5 = 1$$
$$6 - 1 = 5$$
$$6 - 4 = 2 \qquad 6 - 6 = 0$$
$$6 - 2 = 4 \qquad 6 - 0 = 6$$

Continue this activity with the following answers: 12, 4, 9, 14, 18, 13. Allow ample time for students to write addition problems and the related subtraction problems. Ask them to describe the relationship between addition and subtraction. Can they relate this to real-life examples?

Subtraction Facts

SB p. 78

Lesson Objectives

- memorize and practice the subtraction facts
- write and solve subtraction equations

Activity
One-Minute Speed Drills

Purpose: reinforce the ideas in the lesson

Materials

- PCM 17: Subtraction Speed Drills, p. 58
- timer

What to Do

Use the speed drills one at a time as a class warm-up. This should encourage students to memorize the basic subtraction facts.

Distribute copies of PCM 17 facedown. Allow students one minute to complete the assigned drill. Let students check their own drill as you read the correct answers. (*Note:* Fill in the answers on your own copy of PCM 17 to create an answer key.)

Each drill is harder than the previous one. Use your best judgment about how often to administer the drills and whether to repeat any of them. Students should save their unanswered drills for future class use.

Subtracting Larger Numbers

SB p. 80

Lesson Objectives

- subtract larger numbers by lining up like place values
- use estimation to approximate an answer and to check if the exact answer makes sense
- understand when to use zero as a placeholder in subtraction

Activity
Show Your Work

Purpose: extend the ideas in the lesson

Materials

- PCM 18: Show Your Work, p. 59

What to Do

Distribute a copy of PCM 18 to each student. Model the process of subtracting large numbers with no re-grouping. Stress the importance of zero as a place-holder. Using the example on PCM 18, ask why the zero in 504 is important. Have students work on the problems individually. Ask them to use symbols like those in the example to describe what happens in subtraction. Students should be prepared to explain their answers. Problems 11–12 extend the subtraction to numbers with labels. Discuss the answers.

Deciding to Add or Subtract
Problem Solver

SB p. 82

Lesson Objectives
- distinguish between the addition and subtraction operations
- practice decision-making in problem solving

Activity
Deciding What to Do

Purpose: extend the ideas in the lesson

Materials
- (optional) overhead transparency of Texas map
- copies of maps of your state or a nearby state

What to Do

1. Have students form groups of three or four and work on student book page 83, "Making Connections: Planning a Vacation." Allow about 20 minutes, and then discuss the answers using the map of Texas to lead the discussion, if desired. Ask, *"How did you decide whether to add or subtract for each question?"* Let them describe their steps.

2. Distribute a map of your state or a nearby state to each small group. Ask each group to plan and map out a five- to seven-day trip. They should include estimates of expenses such as hotel accommodations, meals, mileage, and transportation. The last step might be to ask them to shorten the trip by a day and find new estimates.

Subtracting by Regrouping

SB p. 84

Lesson Objective
- become familiar with regrouping in subtraction

Activity
Regrouping in Subtraction

Purpose: introduce the ideas in the lesson

Materials
- PCM 12: Regrouping Chart, p. 53
- overhead transparency of PCM 12 and marker

What to Do

On an overhead transparency of PCM 12, model regrouping in subtraction using $745 - 16 = 729$

Operation				
Subtract	Thousands	Hundreds	Tens	Ones
31				X X X X X X X X
745 −16 729		X X X X X X X	X X X Ⓧ	X X X X X
		7	2	9

Regroup →

1. Place the correct number of counters (X's) in each place value to represent 745.

2. Subtract the ones column. Since 6 counters can't be subtracted from 5 counters, regroup 1 counter from the tens place value. The regrouped amount equals 10 ones. Show this amount using 10 counters in the ones column and subtract.

3. Continue subtracting columns from right to left until all columns are subtracted. Regroup whenever the top number is less than the bottom one.

4. Demonstrate regrouping with the subtraction equation in the far left column of the regrouping chart shown above. Emphasize that writing the regrouped amounts above the place value columns helps to ensure accuracy.

5. Ask students to put into their own words what happened in the problem. Give them time to ask questions. Compare addition regrouping (10 becomes 1 of a higher place value) with subtraction regrouping (1 becomes 10 of a lower place value).

Distribute copies of PCM 12 to all students. Have them work in groups of three or four on the following problems:

$$
\begin{array}{r} 576 \\ -\ 38 \\ \hline (538) \end{array}
\qquad
\begin{array}{r} 42 \\ -\ 29 \\ \hline (13) \end{array}
\qquad
\begin{array}{r} 714 \\ -\ 362 \\ \hline (352) \end{array}
$$

$$
\begin{array}{r} 222 \\ -\ 116 \\ \hline (106) \end{array}
\qquad
\begin{array}{r} 4{,}185 \\ -\ 924 \\ \hline (3{,}261) \end{array}
\qquad
\begin{array}{r} 3{,}147 \\ -\ 1{,}626 \\ \hline (1{,}521) \end{array}
$$

Ask each student to choose one problem to demonstrate to their group. Students should take turns demonstrating and explaining to others in the group.

To further explore regrouping in subtraction, write these problems on the board:

$$
\begin{array}{r} \overset{4}{\cancel{5}}\text{ yards }\overset{4}{\cancel{1}}\text{ foot} \\ -\ 2\text{ yards }2\text{ feet} \\ \hline (2\text{ yards }2\text{ feet}) \end{array}
\qquad
\begin{array}{r} \overset{7}{\cancel{8}}\text{ feet }\overset{17}{\cancel{5}}\text{ inches} \\ -\ 4\text{ feet }6\text{ inches} \\ \hline (3\text{ feet }11\text{ inches}) \end{array}
$$

$$
\begin{array}{r} \overset{1}{\cancel{2}}\text{ hours }\overset{88}{\cancel{28}}\text{ minutes} \\ -\ 1\text{ hour }50\text{ minutes} \\ \hline (0\text{ hours }38\text{ minutes}) \end{array}
$$

Ask if someone would like to explain how to regroup these subtraction problems. Ask, *"How do the units of measure affect the regrouping?"* (With units of measure, we regroup the number of smaller units it takes to equal 1 larger unit. For example, 1 yard could be regrouped as 3 feet.)

Regrouping More than Once

SB p. 88

Lesson Objective
- practice regrouping more than once in subtraction

Activity
Investigating Subtraction

Purpose: investigate the ideas in the lesson

Materials
- PCM 12: Regrouping Chart, p. 53
- PCM 19: Investigating Subtraction, p. 60

What to Do

Distribute a copy of PCM 12 and PCM 19 to each student. Let students work in pairs to explore regrouping more than once using the regrouping chart on PCM 12 and the problems on PCM 19. Have each student demonstrate to a partner one of the problems from the handout. When students have had sufficient time to explore, call them together and ask them to describe any patterns or rules they have found. As students describe their discoveries, record the findings on the board or a flip chart. For example:

$$
\begin{array}{r} 35 \\ -\ 20 \\ \hline 15 \end{array}
\quad \text{so} \quad
\begin{array}{r} 35 \\ -\ 19 \\ \hline 16 \end{array}
$$

Because 19 is one less than 20, the answer 16 is one more than 15.

$$
\begin{array}{r} 63\ +\ 5\ =\ \ \ 68 \\ -\ 35\ +\ 5\ =\ -\ 40 \\ \hline 28 \qquad\qquad 28 \end{array}
$$

If you add the same number to both numbers, the difference remains the same.

What Do I Need to Find?
Problem Solver

SB p. 90

Lesson Objectives
- identify the question being asked in a word problem
- use problem-solving strategies

Activity
Understanding the Question

Purpose: extend the ideas in the lesson

Materials
- PCM 20: Understanding the Question, p. 61

What to Do

1. As a class, discuss "What Do I Need to Find?" on student book pages 90–91. Distribute a copy of PCM 20 to each student. Have students underline the question in each problem. They should not solve the problems yet.

2. Working in pairs, have students write equations to represent the questions. The equations should include variables. Students should analyze the problems, looking for similarities and differences, and then solve them.

3. Bring the class together to discuss the problems. Ask students to relate these problems to real experiences in their lives. How did they make their decisions? Check their calculations. Do their answers make sense? Can the equations be written in more than one way? For example, in problem 1, $P + 36 = 714$, or $714 - P = 36$, or $714 - 36 = P$. Is P a good variable to use?

Subtracting from Zeros

SB p. 92

Lesson Objective
- practice regrouping with zeros

Activity
Healthy Living

Purpose: reinforce the ideas in the lesson

Materials
- PCM 21: Calories, p. 62
- PCM 22: Healthy Living, p. 63

What to Do

Distribute a copy of PCM 21 and PCM 22 to each student. Allow students time to glance through the information. Begin a class discussion in which students express their views on topics such as healthy eating habits, exercise, and fat and calorie intake.

Give students the following instructions:

1. *Use the Calories in Common Foods table to fill in the calorie column for Martin.* Remind students that the serving size will affect the number of calories for each food.

2. *Add the numbers to find Martin's total daily intake.*

3. *Use the information found on PCM 21 to answer the questions on PCM 22.*

After sufficient time has elapsed, call the class together for further discussion. Ask students to demonstrate how addition and subtraction were useful in filling out the table.

Subtracting Dollars and Cents

SB p. 94

Lesson Objective
- subtract money amounts by lining up place values

Common Difficulties

Students will need to practice subtracting when zeros are involved. Discuss the tips on student book page 94 and show more examples for each tip. You might ask students to generate examples.

Activity
Tracking Vacation Spending

Purpose: reinforce the ideas in the lesson

What to Do

Allow students time to complete the vacation spending chart on student book page 95 individually. Let them compare and correct answers with a partner. Ask for volunteers to demonstrate at the board how to get each answer. Ask them to explain each step.

Understanding Your Paycheck
Application

SB p. 96

Lesson Objective
- understand a paycheck stub

Activity
Understanding Your Paycheck

Purpose: reinforce the ideas in the lesson

What to Do

Discuss student book page 96. Point out the different parts of a check stub. Answer any questions students may have. Go over the questions in part A at the top of page 97. Then pair students to do part B on page 97. Ask them to answer the questions in part A again, this time using the check stub they completed in part B.

Subtracting on a Calculator
Tools

SB p. 98

Lesson Objective

- practice subtracting on a calculator

Activity
Subtracting on a Calculator

Purpose: reinforce the ideas in the lesson

Materials

- index cards
- calculators

What to Do

1. Distribute a calculator and an index card to each student. Ask students to write two subtraction problems, one on each side of the index card. The first problem should be one that involves large numbers. An example could be 25,605 − 4,799. The second problem should be one that involves money, such as $856 − $48.35.

2. Each student should then pass the index card to another student, who will use a calculator to find the answers and record them on the card. The card is then returned to the student who wrote the problems, who checks the answers with a calculator.

3. Move among the students asking how they got their answers. Have them show you how they used their calculators to find the answers.

Expansion/Reinforcement: Make and distribute some cards with problems that cover the points on student book page 98.

Using the Casio *fx*-260 for the GED

On the Casio calculator, the subtraction key is located to the right of the addition key. On many other calculators, this key is located above the addition key. Refer students to the Casio image on student book page 222.

Figuring Change
Application

SB p. 100

Lesson Objective

- figure change

Activity
Figuring and Making Change

Purpose: extend the ideas in the lesson

Materials

- PCM 2: Bills and Coins, p. 43
- 8% tax table, SB p. 68
- catalogs and flyers

What to Do

1. Place students in groups of three. Distribute sufficient bills and coins, catalogs and flyers, and calculators to each group. One student will be the "buyer." Another student will be the "seller." The third student, the "bookkeeper," will record and check the transactions.

2. Ask the students to make four transactions. The buyer may purchase one or more items on each transaction. The seller will total the purchases and add tax. The buyer will pay with bills and coins totaling either the exact amount or more. The seller will make change. The bookkeeper will record the transactions under five columns, headed: *Price, Tax, Total, Amount Paid,* and *Amount of Change.*

3. Switch the roles and repeat the activity. Move among the groups asking them to explain what they are doing. Encourage them to use rounding and estimating to make decisions.

Gridding in Answers
Tools

SB p. 102

Lesson Objectives

- fill in whole-number answers on a five-column grid
- add and subtract whole numbers

Activity
High and Low

Purpose: reinforce the ideas in the lesson

Materials

- PCM 4: Five-Column Grids, p. 45
- small index cards (5 per student)

What to Do

Use a paper cutter to cut the index cards in half and give 10 halves to each student. Have students write the digits from 0 to 9 on the cards. Also distribute a copy of PCM 4 to each student.

Have students work in pairs. To play the game, each pair should combine and shuffle their cards and place them in a stack facedown. Have each student draw six cards and turn them faceup. Instruct the students to use their cards to make two 3-digit numbers. Students <u>may not</u> start a number with 0. Have them add the two numbers and grid the total on PCM 4. Then have them subtract to find the difference between the numbers and grid the answer on PCM 4.

Next, have students put the deck back together and reshuffle the cards. Partners should now draw eight cards each and repeat the activity using 4-digit numbers.

Repeat the same steps for another 4-digit activity, and then repeat the steps for an activity using 5-digit numbers. For the final grid, have the students find the difference between the highest and lowest numbers on grids 1–8. The winner is the student with the highest number in the final grid.

Expansion/Reinforcement: This activity lets students demonstrate their understanding of place value as they make high and low numbers. For the final grid, you could instead have students find the difference between the two lowest numbers on grids 1–8. The winner would then be the student with the lowest number in the final grid.

Unit 4 Multiplication

Unit Overview

The purpose of this unit is to develop a reliable multiplication background. Success in mathematics will come more easily with the ability to easily recall the multiplication facts. The number line and a multiplication table will be used to help students understand multiplication. Problem-solving strategies, calculators, estimation, and real-life applications will be used to strengthen multiplication skills.

When Do I Multiply? page 107

Use the problems on this page to help students recognize the relationship between addition and multiplication. Ask students to think of other counting patterns. How are they related to addition? To help students understand the relationships, have them keep track of the number of 2s it takes to add up to 10. Then point out that with multiplication, you know that five 2s equal 10 without counting.

Talk About It page 107

Distribute six index cards to each student. Have them put the six most often missed multiplication facts on one side and answers on the back. They can take these home to practice. Emphasize that they must practice these facts outside of class as well as in class. Discuss strategies for learning these facts.

Working Together page 141

Ask students to take a minute to think how they would use the concert tickets. Some suggestions could be tickets for family, friends, or group events. Ask what type of concert they are interested in seeing. Have they been to a concert recently? What were some of the costs? Let them use a calculator as they fill out the ticket order form.

Activity Overview

To find general information about *Math Sense*, including scope and sequence charts, see www.math-sense.com.

Student Book Lesson	Pages in SB	TRG	Activity Type	PCM Number
Building a Multiplication Table	108	26	Investigating Patterns	9
Multiplication Strategies	110	26	Mental Arithmetic	23
Multiplication Facts	112	26	Skill Building	24
Multiplying by One-Digit Numbers	114	27	Hands-On/Reasoning	25
Multiplying and Regrouping	116	27	Hands-On	12
Multiples of 10	118	28	Just for Fun	26
Multiplying by Two-Digit Numbers	120	29	Cooperative Learning	27
What Information Do I Need?	122	29	Reasoning	
Multiplying by Larger Numbers	126	30	Investigation	
Area and Volume	128	30	Drawing/Visualization	9
Multiplying Dollars and Cents	130	31	Problem Solving	28
Multiplying on a Calculator	132	32	Hands-On	
Multistep Problems	134	32	Problem Solving	9, 29
Filling Out an Order Form	136	32	Hands-On	
Gridding Strategies	138	33	Grid Activity	4, 30

Building a Multiplication Table
Tools

SB p. 108

Lesson Objectives
- use a multiplication table to identify multiplication facts
- explore patterns in multiplication

Activity
Building a Multiplication Table

Purpose: reinforce the ideas in the lesson

Materials
- PCM 9: Grid, p. 50

What to Do

Distribute a copy of PCM 9 to each student. Let students work with a partner as they each follow the instructions on student book page 108 to create a multiplication table. Reinforce the role of counting in multiplication. Tell them to use the table and prior knowledge to complete the questions on student book page 109. As a lead-in to the next lesson, ask what patterns they see in the table.

Multiplication Strategies
Problem Solver

SB p. 110

Lesson Objectives
- picture multiplication on the number line
- learn the commutative property of multiplication
- recognize multiples of 2, 5, and 10
- explore patterns in multiples of 9

Activity
I Have, Who Has?

Purpose: extend the ideas in the lesson

Materials
- PCM 23: I Have, Who Has?, p. 64
- index cards

What to Do
1. To reinforce learning multiples, practice counting. Ask volunteers to count out loud by twos, threes, fours, and so on. Ask the remaining students to write down the numbers as volunteers count out loud. Counting by twos, fives, and tens should be easy for students. Other multiples will be more difficult, but keep encouraging students, and have fun with the counting. If students get stuck counting, tell them to add the number they are counting by to the last number they said. For example, to get the next multiple of 7 after 49, use $49 + 7 = 56$.

2. For more practice, write or paste the "I Have, Who Has?" lines on PCM 23 onto separate index cards. Shuffle the cards and distribute all of them. Some students will have more cards than others. Any student may begin by reading from any card, "Who has ____ times ____?" The student with the answer responds by reading, "I have ____, who has ____ times ____?" This activity promotes good listening skills as well as mental arithmetic.

Multiplication Facts

SB p. 112

Lesson Objectives
- memorize and practice the multiplication facts
- write and solve multiplication equations
- use variables in multiplication equations

Activity
One-Minute Speed Drills

Purpose: reinforce the ideas in the lesson

Materials
- PCM 24: Multiplication Speed Drills, p. 65
- timer

What to Do

Use speed drills one at a time as a class warm-up. This should encourage students to memorize the basic multiplication facts.

Distribute copies of PCM 24 facedown. Allow students one minute to complete the assigned drill. Let students check their own drills as you read the correct answers. (*Note:* Fill in the answers on your own copy of PCM 24 to create an answer key.)

Each drill is harder than the previous one. Use your best judgment about how often to administer the drills and whether to repeat any of them. Students should save their unanswered drills for future class use.

Multiplying by One-Digit Numbers

SB p. 114

Lesson Objectives

- multiply by one-digit numbers
- multiply three or more numbers

Activity
Working with Equations

Purpose: extend the ideas in the lesson

Materials

- PCM 25: Understanding Equations, p. 66
- box of toothpicks

What to Do

Pair the students and have each student take at least 30 toothpicks. Distribute a copy of PCM 25 to each student and give the following instructions:

1. *Solve equations one to six. Use your knowledge of addition, subtraction, and multiplication to make each equation true.*
   Example: $3 + n = 8$, $n = 5$

2. *Write a sentence to match the equation.*
   Example: 3 plus what number equals 8?

3. *Using the toothpicks, lay them out in a pattern indicated by the equation.*
   Example: $3 + 5 = 8$ /// + ///// = ////////
   (Draw "toothpicks" on the board.)

4. *Discuss problems seven to thirteen with a partner. Think of as many solutions as possible. Can you think of sentences that match the equations?*

What to Look For

Students should be able to distinguish whether an equation involves addition, subtraction, or multiplication. Make sure that the way they group the toothpicks clearly restates the equation. Equations 7–11 have multiple solutions. Ask students how equations 12 and 13 are related ($y + y + y = 3y$) and if there are multiple solutions (no). Point out that the value of a variable can vary from equation to equation. For example, b will not have the same value in every equation. However, the y's in equation 12 all have the same value.

Multiplying and Regrouping

SB p. 116

Lesson Objective

- become familiar with regrouping in multiplication

Activity
Regrouping in Multiplication

Purpose: reinforce the ideas in the lesson

Materials

- PCM 12: Regrouping Chart, p. 53
- overhead transparency of PCM 12 and marker

What to Do

On an overhead transparency of PCM 12, model regrouping in multiplication using $114 \times 5 = 570$.

	Operation				
	Multiply	Thousands	Hundreds	Tens	Ones
Regroup →	2			X X ←	
	114 ×5 570		X X X X X	X X X X X	X X X X X X X X X X X X X X X X X X X X
			5	7	0

1. Place the correct number of counters (X's) in each place value to represent 114.

2. Repeat the counters 5 times.

3. Working from right to left, total the amount in each place value. Regroup when necessary, always going from right to left.

4. Demonstrate regrouping with the multiplication equation in the far left column of the regrouping chart shown on page 27. Emphasize that writing the regrouped 10s above the tens column helps to ensure accuracy.

5. Ask students to put into their own words what happened in the problem. Give them time to ask questions.

6. Show an example of regrouping more than once using $346 \times 3 = 1,038$.

Operation

Multiply	Thousands	Hundreds	Tens	Ones
Regroup → 1 1	X ←	X ←	X ←	
346 ×3 1,038		X X X X X X X X X	X X X X X X X X X X X X	X X X X X X X X X X X X X X X X X X
	1	0	3	8

Distribute copies of PCM 12 to all students. Write the following problems on the blackboard, and have students solve them in small groups. Ask each student to demonstrate one problem to the group.

305	141	28
× 2	× 5	× 4
(610)	(705)	(112)

569	1,004	2,074
× 3	× 6	× 3
(1,707)	(6,024)	(6,222)

For more exploration of regrouping, have students try these problems:

7 hours 30 minutes
× 5
(35 hours 150 minutes =
37 hours 30 minutes)

1 week 3 days
× 3
(3 weeks 9 days =
4 weeks 2 days)

5 feet 6 inches
× 4
(20 feet 24 inches =
22 feet)

Multiples of 10

SB p. 118

Lesson Objectives

- multiply by multiples of 10

- use estimation to approximate an answer and to check if the exact answer makes sense

Activity ——
Dominos

Purpose: extend the ideas in the lesson

Materials

- PCM 26: Dominos, p. 67, or a set of commercially made dominos

What to Do

You may play this game with two, three, or four players. Follow these modified rules:

1. Place dominos face down and mix them up.

2. Each player chooses seven dominos. The player can look at them but should not show other players. Any remaining dominos are left facedown.

3. The player with the highest double (for example, two 4s) plays first by laying that domino faceup, vertically, on the table. Play then continues with players alternating turns.

4. In order to play, a player must place a domino with a matching number of spots in line, end to end, with the previously placed dominos. He may play on either end of the line. Players may play off the sides of only the first double played.

5. If a player doesn't have a matching domino, she must draw from the pile until she is able to play. If there is no pile, she must pass.

6. To score, the player adds the ends of the dominos. Only if the sum is a multiple of 5 does he get the score.

Example:

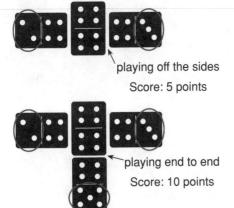

playing off the sides
Score: 5 points

playing end to end
Score: 10 points

7. The round ends when one player has no more dominos. That player scores 5 points for going out first plus the score on the opponents' unplayed dominos rounded to the nearest 5 points. If all play is blocked, score whatever points players already have.

8. Then the next round starts and all dominos are put back into play. The game is over when a player reaches 150 points.

Multiplying by Two-Digit Numbers

SB p. 120

Lesson Objective
• multiply by two-digit numbers

Activity
Multiple Solutions

Purpose: investigate the ideas in the lesson

Materials
• PCM 27: Multiple Solutions, p. 68
• markers
• flip chart pages
• tape

What to Do

Have students form groups of three or four. Distribute flip chart pages, markers, and a copy of

PCM 27 to each group. Have each group work on one of the three problems on PCM 27. They should answer the questions and prepare to explain their work to the rest of the class using the flip chart pages and markers. Then they should develop another question, based on the information in their problem, for the class to answer.

When the groups are ready, tape the pages on the walls and ask a group to volunteer to make the first presentation. Then the class can solve the question the group has written. Ask these questions about the problem: *"Is it clear? Is there enough information to solve the problem? Is it too easy or too hard? Is this the only way to solve the problem? Was estimation a useful tool in solving the problem? Why or why not?"* Compliment students on their creative efforts.

What Information Do I Need?
Problem Solver

SB p. 122

Lesson Objective
• find the necessary information to solve a problem

Common Difficulties

The numbers necessary to solve a problem are not always obvious. Words such as *once, pair,* and *triple* have numerical value. Brainstorm a list of all the words that students can think of that indicate an amount. Discuss these words with the students. This will make them more aware of such words in problems.

Activity
Necessary Information

Purpose: reinforce the ideas in the lesson

What to Do

Using student book pages 122 and 123, ask students to read problems 1–8 and list the necessary information for each question. Students should not solve the problems. Ask, *"What extra information do you see? Would someone like to show how to do problem one on the blackboard?"* Ask for comments from the class. Continue with problems 2–8.

Let students individually develop a story from the information in "Making Connections: Buying in Quantity" on student book page 123. Ask for a few volunteers to tell their stories. Discuss question 3.

Multiplying by Larger Numbers

SB p. 126

Lesson Objectives

- use partial products when multiplying by larger numbers
- multiply using the short form

Common Difficulties

Students may find it difficult to eliminate the unnecessary zeros when multiplying and to keep the place values lined up. Let them know that it is not necessary to use the short form. However, a class discussion about the differences and similarities between the long form and short form may help students become more comfortable using the short form.

Activity
The Long and the Short of It

Purpose: introduce the ideas in the lesson

What to Do

1. Put this problem on the board: 475×506

2. Estimate the answer: $500 \times 500 = 250,000$

3. Multiply in long form as on the left. Then multiply in short form as on the right.

$$
\begin{array}{r}
475 \\
\times\ 506 \\
\hline
2850 \\
000 \\
2375 \\
\hline
240,350
\end{array}
\qquad
\begin{array}{r}
475 \\
\times\ 506 \\
\hline
2850 \\
23750 \\
\hline
240,350
\end{array}
$$

4. Discuss the similarities and differences between the two forms of multiplication. Ask, *"What things are the same in long form and short form?"* (the partial product 2,850, the answer, etc.) *"What are the differences?"* (In the short form, fewer zeros are used, the partial product 2,375 moves up, etc.). Ask other

questions such as, *"Does this change the answer? Are the answers close to the estimate? Is the zero in two thousand eight hundred fifty important? Why or why not?"*

5. Copy the following problems onto the board. Tell students there are commonly made mistakes in these problems. See if students can point out what's wrong.

$$
\begin{array}{r}
475 \\
\times\ 506 \\
\hline
2,850 \\
23,750 \\
\hline
26,600
\end{array}
\qquad
\begin{array}{r}
475 \\
\times\ 506 \\
\hline
2,850 \\
2,375 \\
\hline
5,225
\end{array}
$$

Ask students, *"How can your estimate help you realize you need to rethink your steps?"* Repeat this process with another problem.

What to Look For

When multiplying, students should first estimate the answer and then compare their exact answer to the estimate. Have students do part A on student book page 126 and check their work first against an estimate and then with a calculator. Completing the cross number puzzle on student book page 127 will help students review all of these skills.

Area and Volume
Application

SB p. 128

Lesson Objectives

- find the area of squares and rectangles
- find the volume of rectangular containers

Activity
Drawing It Out

Purpose: investigate the ideas in the lesson

Materials

- PCM 9: Grid, p. 50
- overhead transparency of PCM 9 and marker

What to Do

Begin a group discussion about measurements of length, width, and height. Use the following as a guideline for the discussion.

1. Length is a one-dimensional measurement. Ask, *"What units do we commonly use to measure the length of a line?"* (feet, inches, meters, miles, etc.). Draw some of these actual lengths on the board. Ask, *"What items in this room do we buy by length?"* (molding around the ceiling, framework around a bulletin board, baseboard, trim on any item). *"Do you recall what we call the measurement of the distance around a geometric figure?"* (perimeter) *"How do you find perimeter?"* (add the lengths of the sides). Perimeter actually outlines or frames a figure.

2. Area is a two-dimensional measurement. When multiplying length and width, the result is surface area. Ask, *"What units measure surface area?"* (square inches, square feet, square meters, square miles, etc.). Draw a few examples on the board. Ask, *"What items in this room would require measuring the surface area before purchasing?"* (floor tile, carpeting, paint, and wallpaper).

3. Volume is a three-dimensional measurement. Multiply length by width by height to find the amount of space in a container like a box. Units that measure volume are cubic inches, cubic yards, cubic meters, etc. Ask, *"What items would you purchase by the cubic unit?"* (sand, concrete, refrigerator, containers like boxes, etc.). *"What does it mean on a cereal box when it says that it's packed by weight, not by volume?"* (The cereal box is packed by how much its contents weigh, not by the volume it can hold.)

4. Illustrate the relationship between perimeter and area on the overhead transparency of PCM 9. Draw a rectangle that is 3 units by 4 units. Ask, *"What is the perimeter?"* (14 units) *"What is the area?"* (12 square units) *"Can you draw any other rectangles that have an area of twelve square units?"* (1 × 12 and 2 × 6). Say, *"Find the perimeter of each of these figures."* Distribute a copy of PCM 9 to each student. Let students explore area and perimeter on their own papers with figures that have areas of 8, 16, or 24 square units.

Multiplying Dollars and Cents

SB p. 130

Lesson Objective

- multiply money amounts

Activity
Solving Money Problems

Purpose: investigate the ideas in the lesson

Materials

- PCM 28: Problem Solving with Money, p. 69

What to Do

Tell students that this activity combines problem solving with a time limit. The activity goes like this:

1. Tell students that they will receive a handout and will have five minutes to read and study the problems. Stress that they are to only think about how to solve the problems. They should not write at this point.

2. Distribute copies of PCM 28 to all students. Give students five minutes to read and organize their thoughts.

3. Give students five minutes to answer the questions.

4. Then give them five minutes with a partner to share, expand, correct, or change their answers.

5. As a class, discuss all answers. Commend students when they find an answer that no one else has found. Be enthusiastic about the wide variety of answers.

What to Look For

This activity can be used to encourage students to look for more than one answer to a problem. Discuss why a particular answer might be preferred over another answer. For instance, would students rather have a $20 bill or two $5 bills and a $10 bill? Let the students explore their feelings about working under a time limit. Ask, *"Are there situations in real life when you're under a time limit to solve a problem?"*

Multiplying on a Calculator
Tools

SB p. 132

Lesson Objectives
- practice multiplying on a calculator
- use estimation to check answers

Activity
Multiplying on a Calculator

Purpose: reinforce the ideas in the lesson

Materials
- calculators

What to Do
1. Ask students to each generate a multiplication problem. Write one problem at a time on the board. All students should estimate the answer and write the equation and their estimate on their paper. Example: $15{,}765 \times 98$

   Estimate: $16{,}000 \times 100 = 1{,}600{,}000$

2. Write a sampling of students' estimates next to the problem on the board. Now ask all students to use their calculators to find the actual answer. (The answer to the example above is 1,544,970.) Ask, *"Is this close to the estimate?"* (Yes, because both answers are one million.) Ask the student who generated the problem to read the answer out loud.

3. Then go to the next student who will pose another problem and so on. Encourage students to use relatively large numbers, to use money amounts, and to read their answers aloud. Help them with any problems or questions about calculators.

Using the Casio *fx*-260 for the GED
On the Casio calculator, the four operations keys are located in a block above the equal key. The multiplication key is directly above the addition key. Students can refer to an image of the Casio *fx*-260 calculator on student book page 222.

Multistep Problems
Problem Solver

SB p. 134

Lesson Objective
- use a combination of addition, subtraction, and multiplication skills to solve word problems

Activity
Billboard Advertising

Purpose: extend the ideas in the lesson

Materials
- PCM 9: Grid, p. 50
- PCM 29: Billboard Advertising, p. 69
- calculators

What to Do
Students should form groups of three or four. Distribute a calculator, a copy of PCM 9, and a copy of PCM 29 to each group. Students should work together to answer the questions on PCM 29. Ask them to use the grid to draw the billboards. Encourage them to use a calculator to perform the operations. When the groups have had sufficient time to finish their work, bring them together and discuss the answers.

Filling Out an Order Form
Application

SB p. 136

Lesson Objectives
- become familiar with filling out an order form
- use multiplication and addition to fill out order forms

Activity
Filling Out Order Forms

Purpose: extend the ideas in the lesson

Materials
- calculators
- catalogs or SB pp. 136–137

What to Do

Begin a discussion with students about ordering from a catalog. Let them use catalogs or student book pages 136–137 to calculate and place orders. Discuss methods of delivery and payment, and returns. The students can use calculators to check their answers if they do the arithmetic by hand.

Gridding Strategies
Tools

SB p. 138

Lesson Objective

- fill in answers to word problems on a five-column grid

Activity

Keeping Track of Inventory

Purpose: reinforce the ideas in the lesson

Materials

- PCM 4: Five-Column Grids, p. 45
- PCM 30: Keeping Track of Inventory, p. 70

What to Do

Make one copy of PCM 30 and cut the cards apart. Give each student a copy of PCM 4. Explain that stores must keep an accurate and current record of the stock they have on shelves and in the warehouse.

A company manufactures blank videotapes. The warehouse has 15,080 tapes in stock. Have students enter this number in grid 1 on PCM 4. Tell students that you are going to draw cards at random. The cards describe situations that will affect the inventory. After you read a card, the students should figure out the new number of tapes stored in the warehouse and enter this number in the next grid on PCM 4.

What to Look For

Students may not recognize which situations decrease the inventory and which situations increase it. After each transaction, ask a few students to share their answers. Discuss how the students knew whether to add, subtract, or multiply. If a card requires a series of operations, discuss how the students knew which operations to do first.

Unit 5 Division

Unit Overview

The purpose of this unit is to build strong division skills. The background for division will be built upon the skills developed in earlier units, including counting, using the number line, and working with a multiplication table. Division strategies, such as working with remainders and dividing by multiples of 10, will increase confidence in division skills. Problem solving will be emphasized through applications.

When Do I Divide? page 143

Ask students to think about using division in daily life. On the board, make two columns with the headings "split into equal parts" and "how many times." As students tell how they use division, list their responses under one of the two headings. Some answers might include splitting a bill for lunch, sharing prize money, how many 18-inch pieces can be cut from a roll of tubing, and how many $250 payments it will take to pay off a $5,000 loan.

Talk About It page 143

Discuss the problems. Ask students questions such as, *"How do you know which number is the divisor? Can you name real-life settings where you might use these sentences? What difficulties have you had with division in the past?"* Spend a few minutes practicing setting up division problems three different ways.

Working Together page 175

Bring in newspapers and distribute them to students in small groups. Discuss the different sections of the newspaper. Ask, *"Where would you find temperature listings? Where is the classified section? What does* classified *mean?"* Other questions to ask: *"How did you find the average temperature? What numbers do you think would greatly affect the average? For instance, if nine of the temperatures are in the fifty-five to seventy-five range and one is ninety-two, how does this affect the average? Is it helpful to find the average price for a type of used car?"*

Activity Overview

To find general information about *Math Sense*, including scope and sequence charts, see www.math-sense.com.

Student Book Lesson	Pages in SB	TRG	Activity Type	PCM Number
Division Strategies	144	35	Investigating Patterns	9
Division Facts	146	35	Skill Building	31
Dividing by One Digit	148	35	Hands-On	12
Remainders	150	36	Investigating Patterns	32
Zeros in the Answer	152	37	Estimating	33
Finding an Average	154	37	Reasoning	34
Dividing by Two or More Digits	158	38	Skill Building	
Item Sets	160	39	Writing	35
Dividing Dollars and Cents	162	39	Real-Life Applications	
Dividing on a Calculator	164	39	Reasoning	36
Choosing the Right Operation	166	40	Cooperative Learning	
Finding Unit Price	168	40	Real-Life Applications	
Putting It All Together	170	40	Real-Life Applications	37
Gridding in Division Answers	172	41	Grid Activity	4

Division Strategies
Problem Solver

SB p. 144

Lesson Objectives
- relate division to multiplication facts
- picture division on the number line
- explore patterns in division
- divide by one, divide a number by itself, and divide zero by any number

Activity
Understanding Division

Purpose: investigate the ideas in the lesson

Materials
- PCM 9: Grid, p. 50
- overhead transparency of PCM 9 and marker

What to Do
Distribute copies of PCM 9 to all students. Review the idea of rows and columns. Ask, *"How can you show eighteen divided into equal parts using rows and columns?"* On the overhead transparency, model students' solutions for the class as shown below.

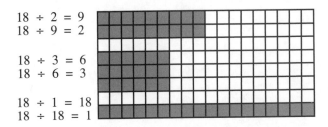

$18 \div 2 = 9$
$18 \div 9 = 2$

$18 \div 3 = 6$
$18 \div 6 = 3$

$18 \div 1 = 18$
$18 \div 18 = 1$

Expand this idea by asking them to show 24, 15, 35, etc., divided into equal parts on their grid. Ask students to explain how these rows and columns represent division.

Division Facts

SB p. 146

Lesson Objectives
- memorize and practice the division facts
- write and solve division equations

Activity
One-Minute Speed Drills

Purpose: reinforce the ideas in the lesson

Materials
- PCM 31: Division Speed Drills, p. 71
- timer

What to Do
Use the speed drills one at a time as a class warm-up. This should encourage students to memorize the basic multiplication facts.

Distribute copies of PCM 31 facedown. Allow students one minute to complete the assigned drill. Let students check their own drill as you read the correct answers. (*Note:* Fill in the answers on your own copy of PCM 31 to create an answer key.)

Each drill is harder than the previous one. Use your best judgment about how often to administer the drills and whether to repeat any of them. Students should save their unanswered drills for future class use.

Dividing by One Digit

SB p. 148

Lesson Objectives
- divide using the four-step process
- divide using short division

Activity
Regrouping in Division

Purpose: reinforce the ideas in the lesson

Materials
- PCM 12: Regrouping Chart, p. 53
- overhead transparency of PCM 12 and marker

What to Do
On an overhead transparency of PCM 12, model dividing by a one-digit number. Use $396 \div 3 = 132$, which has no remainder.

Operation

	Divide	Thousands	Hundreds	Tens	Ones
Regroup →					
	132 3)396 − 3 09 − 9 06 − 6 0		(X X X)	(X X X) (X X X) (X X X)	(X X X) (X X X)
			1	3	2

1. Place the correct number of counters (X's) in each place value to represent the dividend 396.

2. Separate the counters in the hundreds column into groups containing the number indicated by the divisor (3). Circle each group of 3 X's.

3. Working from left to right, repeat the process at each place value.

4. After separating the place values into groups, count the number of groups for each place value. This is the answer.

5. Demonstrate the actual division process using the division equation in the far left column of the regrouping chart. Emphasize that division problems are worked from left to right.

6. Ask students to put into their own words what happened in the problem. Give them time to ask questions.

7. Use the following example to show regrouping to the next lower place value when there aren't enough counters. In this example, 3 will not divide into 2. Regroup 2 hundreds as 20 tens. Then divide. Note that any counters that remained would also be regrouped to the next lower place value.

Operation

	Divide	Thousands	Hundreds	Tens	Ones
Regroup →				(X X X X X X) (X X X) (X X X X X X) (X X X) (X X X X X X) (x)(X X X) (X X)	
	85 3)255 − 24 15 − 15 0		(X X)	(x)(X X X X)(x)(x x)(X X X)	
				8	5

Distribute copies of PCM 12 to all students. Have them work in pairs on the following problems. Ask each student to demonstrate one problem to the class.

$648 \div 2 = (324)$

$84 \div 4 = (21)$

$351 \div 3 = (117)$

$268 \div 2 = (134)$

$749 \div 7 = (107)$

$654 \div 6 = (109)$

$2{,}736 \div 9 = (304)$

$535 \div 5 = (107)$

$783 \div 3 = (261)$

$6{,}636 \div 6 = (1{,}106)$

$9{,}232 \div 4 = (2{,}308)$

Remainders

SB p. 150

Lesson Objectives

- become familiar with remainders
- decide how to use remainders in problem solving

Activity ————
Divisibility

Purpose: extend the ideas in the lesson

Materials

- PCM 32: Hundred Board, p. 72
- paper, pencils, and pens
- three colors of highlighters
- overhead transparency of PCM 32 and marker

What to Do

Use PCM 32 to explore multiples and make conjectures about divisibility. Distribute a copy of PCM 32 to each student. Have students work in groups of three or four. Give them the following directions orally. Use the follow-up questions to guide students' discovery of patterns. Use the overhead transparency of PCM 32 as a reference during the discussion.

1. *Highlight the bottom half of each box containing a multiple of two. What do you notice about these numbers?* (Multiples of 2 are even numbers.)

2. *Use a pencil to circle multiples of three. What do these numbers have in common?* (Every third number is a multiple of 3. They form diagonals across the board.)

3. *Put a check mark in the upper right corner of multiples of six. What is characteristic of these numbers?* (They end in 0, 2, 4, 6, and 8. They are multiples of 2 and 3.)

4. *Put a dot in the upper left corner of multiples of nine. Do these numbers have anything in common?* (They are multiples of 3.)

5. *Use a different color highlighter to put a diagonal slash through multiples of five. How can you recognize these numbers?* (They end in 5 or 0.)

6. *For multiples of ten, fill in the zero with a third highlighter color. What do these numbers have in common?* (They end in 0. They are multiples of 2 and 5.)

7. *Put an X in the lower left corner of multiples of four. How are these numbers similar?* (They end in 0, 2, 4, 6, and 8. They are multiples of 2.)

8. *Put a star in the lower right corner of multiples of eight. What do these numbers have in common?* (They are multiples of 2 and of 4.)

Do students' observations match the rules on student book page 151? Have students test the rules on numbers with three or more digits of their choosing. Ask, *"How can these divisibility rules help you decide whether or not there will be a remainder when you divide?"*

Zeros in the Answer

SB p. 152

Lesson Objectives
- understand when to use zero as a placeholder in division

- practice using short division when zeros appear as placeholders in the answer
- divide by multiples of 10

Activity
Estimating Division

Purpose: extend the ideas in the lesson

Materials
- PCM 33: Estimating Division, p. 73

What to Do

Distribute a copy of PCM 33 to each student. Review estimation and the comparison symbols. Talk about using friendly numbers to make mental division easier. For instance, $234 \div 6$ could be estimated using the division fact $24 \div 6 = 4$. Have students do the problems on PCM 33 by using estimation, not long division. When they have completed the problems, go over the answers, asking students to explain how they rounded their numbers and estimated the quotients. Stress to students that there is no one correct estimate.

Finding an Average
Application

SB p. 154

Lesson Objectives
- become familiar with average
- solve word problems that involve average

Activity
Measures of Central Tendency

Purpose: extend the ideas in the lesson

Materials
- PCM 34: Measures of Central Tendency, p. 73
- self-stick removable notes

What to Do
1. Begin by writing *Measures of Central Tendency* on the board. Point out that you are going to be looking at data and trying to find values that represent the whole set of numbers. Distribute copies of PCM 34 to all students.

2. Collect data from your students. Have students estimate the number of miles from where they are now to where they were born. Have them write the number of miles in large numerals on a self-stick note. You should also do this.

3. Draw a long number line on the board and attach your self-stick note at a point on the line. Then ask students to place their self-stick notes along the line. Remind them that larger numbers go to the right. It may look like this:

4. Have students copy the data onto their handouts under A. Order the Data. They should copy it in order, from lowest to highest.

5. Have students fill in B. Analyze the Data. Give them the following definitions and instructions and have them find and record the information on the lines provided:

   • **Range:** the difference between the largest and smallest values in a set of data. Subtract the shortest distance from the longest distance.
   Example: 4,000 − 20 = 3,980 miles

   • **Mean:** the average of a set of numbers. Add all distances and divide by the number of distances.
   Example: 20 + 30 + 30 + 30 + 75 + 300 + 300 + 900 + 1,200 + 2,000 + 4,000 = 8,885

   8,885 ÷ 11 ≈ 808

   • **Median:** the middle value of a set of data. Find the middle number of the distances as ordered from smallest to largest. In this example, 300 is the middle number, being sixth out of 11 numbers. If there are an even number of distances, average the two middle distances to find the median.

   • **Mode:** the value that occurs most frequently in a set of data. Find the number that occurs the most often. There may be no mode or more than one mode. In this example, the mode is 30 because this response appears three times.

6. Discuss the questions in C. Evaluate the Data. You might also ask, *"When would you find the average?"* (bowling scores). *"When would the median be a good indicator?"* (median age in a group, because it ignores extremes). *"When would the mode be important?"* (to find the most popular amount of something).

Dividing by Two or More Digits

SB p. 158

Lesson Objective
• practice using educated guessing and estimation when dividing by two or more digits

Activity
Dividing on Graph Paper

Purpose: reinforce the ideas in the lesson

Materials
• graph paper

What to Do
Here are two things to do to help students solve the problems on student book page 158:

1. Have students do the problems on graph paper. It will help them line up the place values.

2. Make sure students estimate the answers before they actually divide. Have them write their estimate next to each problem on the graph paper.

Example:

				2	1	6	R	5	0					
	7	5	1	6,	2	5	0				Estimate:			
			1	5	0						1	6,	2	5	0	÷	7	5
				1	2	5								
					7	5				1	6,	0	0	Ø
					5	0	0					8	Ø	= 2 0 0
					4	5	0							
						5	0							

Item Sets

SB p. 160

Lesson Objectives

- choose the information needed to solve a problem
- practice problem solving using charts and realia

Activity
The Chicago Connection

Purpose: extend the ideas in the lesson

Materials

- PCM 35: The Chicago Connection, p. 74
- calculators

What to Do

Distribute a copy of PCM 35 to each student. Let students work in pairs to write at least four problems from the information given. They may want to use all four operations and write multistep problems.

Urge students to write clearly and develop problems that use the information given on the handout. Have them exchange papers and solve each other's problems on separate paper. Discuss the problems as a group. Encourage students to use calculators.

Expansion/Reinforcement: Collect the problems and compile them into a set. Print the entire group of problems, and give them to the students to solve. Have students analyze both the language and mathematical aspects. Ask, *"Do the questions make sense? Do they apply to the information given?"*

Dividing Dollars and Cents

SB p. 162

Lesson Objective

- divide money amounts

Activity
Time Payments

Purpose: extend the ideas in the lesson

Materials

- newspaper and circular advertisements

What to Do

Discuss time payments. Ask, *"What kind of items can be purchased on time? What is a down payment? Are there other costs when you pay in installments?"* Talk about interest in a general way—relate it to taxes and refer to the activity on taxes in unit 2, student book page 68. Taxes and interest are both added costs.

Ask students to look through the advertisements and choose a few items to purchase on time. On their papers, they should list their purchases, the down payment, and the length of the payment plan. Then they should calculate how much it will cost per payment and the difference between paying cash and paying in installments. Ask students to exchange papers and check each other's calculations. Have them explain their purchases and payment plans to the class.

Dividing on a Calculator

SB p. 164

Lesson Objectives

- practice dividing on a calculator
- use estimation to check answers

Activity
Deciding What to Do with Remainders

Purpose: extend the ideas in the lesson

Materials

- PCM 36: Deciding What to Do with Remainders, p. 75
- calculators

What to Do

Distribute a copy of PCM 36 to each student. Students should work individually on the problems with the aid of a calculator. Upon completion, begin a discussion about using reasoning in conjunction with calculators. Discuss what to do with the remainders and how the remainders affect the answer.

Choosing the Right Operation
Problem Solver

SB p. 166

Lesson Objective

- practice choosing the right operation to solve word problems

Activity
Brainstorming

Purpose: reinforce the ideas in the lesson

Materials

- flip chart pages
- markers
- tape

What to Do

Begin a discussion about brainstorming. Tell students it means opening up their minds and exploring all the possibilities about a topic. Ideas are recorded by simply listing them as they are generated.

You might model the following brainstorming list for the topic "Problem Solving" on a flip chart:

> identify the question
>
> personalize the problem
>
> look for words with meaning
>
> calculate
>
> choose the operation
>
> find the necessary information
>
> identify unnecessary information
>
> multistep problem?
>
> use estimation
>
> does the answer make sense?
>
> reread the problem
>
> check answer

Have students work in small groups to brainstorm about "Math in My Life." Distribute flip chart pages and markers to each group. Have the groups put their lists on flip chart pages. When they are done, hang the pages on the wall and let each group talk about their list.

Finding Unit Price
Application

SB p. 168

Lesson Objective

- use division to find unit price

Activity
Finding Unit Price

Purpose: reinforce the ideas in the lesson

Materials

- calculators

What to Do

Discuss unit pricing. Ask, *"Have you seen unit prices in stores? Why is unit price important?"*

Tiff Peanut Butter	Kippy Peanut Butter	ShopTown Peanut Butter	Kippy Peanut Butter
$1.89	$3.90	$4.80	$5.39
8 oz.	16 oz.	32 oz.	32 oz.
(.24/oz.)	(.24/oz.)	(.15/oz.)	(.17/oz.)

1. List each of the peanut butter brands with its respective price and size. Don't list the unit price. Ask students, *"Which brand costs the most? Why do you think Kippy is listed twice with two prices?"* (different sizes).

2. Next list the size of each of the products under discussion. Ask, *"Which peanut butter do you think is the best buy? Did the size influence your choice?"*

3. Then have students use calculators to find the unit price for each peanut butter listed.

4. Have students compare unit prices and choose the brand and size that is cheapest per ounce.

Putting It All Together

SB p. 170

Lesson Objective

- use skills, tools, and reasoning to solve problems

Common Difficulties

Because percents are used so much in advertising, introduce using the percent key on the calculator. Let students practice by finding 25% of an item that cost $58 and an item that costs $19.95. Have them enter the following keys in this order: ⑤ ⑧ ✕ ② ⑤ %. The display will show 14.5. Explain that this equals $14.50. Some students may have to enter the ＝ key to get an answer.

Then have them enter ① ⑨ ⋅ ⑨ ⑤ ✕ ② ⑤ %. The display will show 4.9875, which rounds to $4.99. Discuss what is displayed when the percent key is used.

Using the Casio *fx*-260 for the GED

If students are using the Casio calculator, be sure that they know that they must press the |SHIFT| key followed by the ＝ key to use the % function.

Activity
Redecorating a Kitchen

Purpose: extend the ideas in the lesson

Materials

- PCM 37: Floor Plan, p. 76
- 8% tax table, SB p. 68
- calculators
- newspaper advertisements

What to Do

Have students form groups of three or four. Distribute a copy of PCM 37 and several newspaper advertisements to each group. Tell students that each group has a budget of $5,000. Ask them to select purchases for the home such as flooring, appliances, curtains, table and chairs, paint, wallpaper, baseboards, etc. They should decide which products to buy, determine where to get the best price, and include sales tax in the total cost. They can estimate labor charges or plan to do the work themselves. Encourage students to use measurements as much as possible.

Discussion topics might include quality versus quantity, how to evaluate ads, and how to apply for credit.

Gridding in Division Answers
Tools

SB p. 172

Lesson Objectives

- grid whole numbers and decimals
- decide how to use a remainder

Activity
What's the Chance?

Purpose: extend the ideas in the lesson

Materials

- PCM 4: Five-Column Grids, p. 45
- calculators (optional)

What to Do

Distribute a copy of PCM 4 to each student. In this exercise, students will divide amounts by 3, 4, and 5. They will then decide what to do with the remainder and grid the quotients on PCM 4.

Items 1–3: Make as many teams as you can from 3,860 students. Make teams of 3, 4, and 5 students.

Items 4–6: Separate 18 cups of flour evenly into 3 bowls, 4 bowls, and 5 bowls.

Items 7–9: Suppose the total cost of a laptop computer is $1,579. How much would you pay per month (to the nearest dollar) if you pay it off in 3 months? 4 months? 5 months?

Answers:

1. 1,286	4. 6	7. $526
2. 965	5. 4.5	8. $395
3. 772	6. 3.6	9. $316

What to Look For

Help students understand that the decimal part of the answer is the remainder. You may wish to discuss various situations in which the remainder should be rounded up, used, or discarded.

Thousands Place Value Chart

Ten Thousands	Thousands	Hundreds	Tens	Ones

Bills and Coins

0 _____	26 _____	52 _____	78 _____
1 _____	27 _____	53 _____	79 _____
2 _____	28 _____	54 _____	80 _____
3 _____	29 _____	55 _____	81 _____
4 _____	30 _____	56 _____	82 _____
5 _____	31 _____	57 _____	83 _____
6 _____	32 _____	58 _____	84 _____
7 _____	33 _____	59 _____	85 _____
8 _____	34 _____	60 _____	86 _____
9 _____	35 _____	61 _____	87 _____
10 _____	36 _____	62 _____	88 _____
11 _____	37 _____	63 _____	89 _____
12 _____	38 _____	64 _____	90 _____
13 _____	39 _____	65 _____	91 _____
14 _____	40 _____	66 _____	92 _____
15 _____	41 _____	67 _____	93 _____
16 _____	42 _____	68 _____	94 _____
17 _____	43 _____	69 _____	95 _____
18 _____	44 _____	70 _____	96 _____
19 _____	45 _____	71 _____	97 _____
20 _____	46 _____	72 _____	98 _____
21 _____	47 _____	73 _____	99 _____
22 _____	48 _____	74 _____	100 _____
23 _____	49 _____	75 _____	
24 _____	50 _____	76 _____	
25 _____	51 _____	77 _____	

Five-Column Grids

1.

2.

3.

4.

5.

6.

7.

8.

9.

Calendar Instructions

1. Highlight your birthday.

2. Circle today's date with a pencil.

3. Underline Labor Day, Memorial Day, and Thanksgiving with a pen.

4. Put an *X* on the first Sunday of every month.

5. Highlight the name of the shortest month.

6. Put a box around the date you started this course.

7. Father's Day is the third Sunday in June. Put a star on this day.

8. Mother's Day is the second Sunday in May. Put a heart on Mother's Day.

9. If this is a leap year, put a triangle around the extra day.

10. Circle in red three dates that are important to you.

11. Write the date of your birthday three different ways.

    _____

    _____

    _____

12. How many paychecks do you get per year if your employer pays you
    the 1st and 15th of each month? _____
    once a month? _____
    every other Friday? _____

13. Federal taxes are due on April 15 each year. What day of the week is that this year?

    _____

14. Write the date for Independence Day, using numbers only. _____

15. If friends were married on Valentine's Day, what is the date of their
    anniversary? _____

Checks and Money Orders

290

31-20/213

_____ 20 ___

Pay to
the order of _____ $ [   ]

Dollars

▌ American Bank
  245 Lake Street
  Hometown, IL 60007

Memo _____

I:67   004 I:00-746 II▪

291

31-20/213

_____ 20 ___

Pay to
the order of _____ $ [   ]

Dollars

▌ American Bank
  245 Lake Street
  Hometown, IL 60007

Memo _____

I:67   004 I:00-746 II▪

Your Currency Exchange
1600 W. Grand Ave.
Hometown, IL 60007
555-2055

$\frac{2\text{-}425}{710}$

No. A 171608

_____ 20 ___

Remitter _____

Dollars	Cents

Pay to
the order of _____

Dollars

A.M. Amirth

Grand Check Cashiers, Inc.

State regulated

Clocks

_____ _____ _____ _____ _____

_____ _____ _____ _____ _____

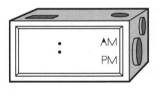

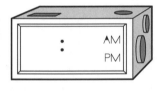

_____ _____ _____

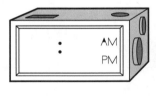

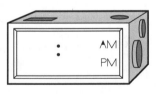

_____ _____ _____

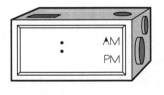
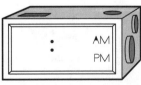
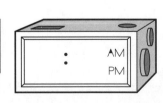
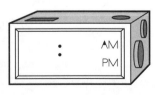

_____ _____ _____ _____

Tax Table

2001 Tax Table—*Continued*   **Caution.** Dependents, see the worksheet on page 33.

23,000 / 24,000 / 25,000

If line 39 (taxable income) is— At least	But less than	And you are— Single	Married filing jointly *	Married filing separately	Head of a household
23,000	**23,050**	3,454	3,454	3,507	3,454
23,050	23,100	3,461	3,461	3,521	3,461
23,100	23,150	3,469	3,469	3,534	3,469
23,150	23,200	3,476	3,476	3,548	3,476
23,200	23,250	3,484	3,484	3,562	3,484
23,250	23,300	3,491	3,491	3,576	3,491
23,300	23,350	3,499	3,499	3,589	3,499
23,350	23,400	3,506	3,506	3,603	3,506
23,400	23,450	3,514	3,514	3,617	3,514
23,450	23,500	3,521	3,521	3,631	3,521
23,500	23,550	3,529	3,529	3,644	3,529
23,550	23,600	3,536	3,536	3,658	3,536
23,600	23,650	3,544	3,544	3,672	3,544
23,650	23,700	3,551	3,551	3,686	3,551
23,700	23,750	3,559	3,559	3,699	3,559
23,750	23,800	3,566	3,566	3,713	3,566
23,800	23,850	3,574	3,574	3,727	3,574
23,850	23,900	3,581	3,581	3,741	3,581
23,900	23,950	3,589	3,589	3,754	3,589
23,950	24,000	3,596	3,596	3,768	3,596
24,000	**24,050**	3,604	3,604	3,782	3,604
24,050	24,100	3,611	3,611	3,796	3,611
24,100	24,150	3,619	3,619	3,809	3,619
24,150	24,200	3,626	3,626	3,823	3,626
24,200	24,250	3,634	3,634	3,837	3,634
24,250	24,300	3,641	3,641	3,851	3,641
24,300	24,350	3,649	3,649	3,864	3,649
24,350	24,400	3,656	3,656	3,878	3,656
24,400	24,450	3,664	3,664	3,892	3,664
24,450	24,500	3,671	3,671	3,906	3,671
24,500	24,550	3,679	3,679	3,919	3,679
24,550	24,600	3,686	3,686	3,933	3,686
24,600	24,650	3,694	3,694	3,947	3,694
24,650	24,700	3,701	3,701	3,961	3,701
24,700	24,750	3,709	3,709	3,974	3,709
24,750	24,800	3,716	3,716	3,988	3,716
24,800	24,850	3,724	3,724	4,002	3,724
24,850	24,900	3,731	3,731	4,016	3,731
24,900	24,950	3,739	3,739	4,029	3,739
24,950	25,000	3,746	3,746	4,043	3,746
25,000	**25,050**	3,754	3,754	4,057	3,754
25,050	25,100	3,761	3,761	4,071	3,761
25,100	25,150	3,769	3,769	4,084	3,769
25,150	25,200	3,776	3,776	4,098	3,776
25,200	25,250	3,784	3,784	4,112	3,784
25,250	25,300	3,791	3,791	4,126	3,791
25,300	25,350	3,799	3,799	4,139	3,799
25,350	25,400	3,806	3,806	4,153	3,806
25,400	25,450	3,814	3,814	4,167	3,814
25,450	25,500	3,821	3,821	4,181	3,821
25,500	25,550	3,829	3,829	4,194	3,829
25,550	25,600	3,836	3,836	4,208	3,836
25,600	25,650	3,844	3,844	4,222	3,844
25,650	25,700	3,851	3,851	4,236	3,851
25,700	25,750	3,859	3,859	4,249	3,859
25,750	25,800	3,866	3,866	4,263	3,866
25,800	25,850	3,874	3,874	4,277	3,874
25,850	25,900	3,881	3,881	4,291	3,881
25,900	25,950	3,889	3,889	4,304	3,889
25,950	26,000	3,896	3,896	4,318	3,896

26,000 / 27,000 / 28,000

If line 39 (taxable income) is— At least	But less than	And you are— Single	Married filing jointly *	Married filing separately	Head of a household
26,000	**26,050**	3,904	3,904	4,332	3,904
26,050	26,100	3,911	3,911	4,346	3,911
26,100	26,150	3,919	3,919	4,359	3,919
26,150	26,200	3,926	3,926	4,373	3,926
26,200	26,250	3,934	3,934	4,387	3,934
26,250	26,300	3,941	3,941	4,401	3,941
26,300	26,350	3,949	3,949	4,414	3,949
26,350	26,400	3,956	3,956	4,428	3,956
26,400	26,450	3,964	3,964	4,442	3,964
26,450	26,500	3,971	3,971	4,456	3,971
26,500	26,550	3,979	3,979	4,469	3,979
26,550	26,600	3,986	3,986	4,483	3,986
26,600	26,650	3,994	3,994	4,497	3,994
26,650	26,700	4,001	4,001	4,511	4,001
26,700	26,750	4,009	4,009	4,524	4,009
26,750	26,800	4,016	4,016	4,538	4,016
26,800	26,850	4,024	4,024	4,552	4,024
26,850	26,900	4,031	4,031	4,566	4,031
26,900	26,950	4,039	4,039	4,579	4,039
26,950	27,000	4,046	4,046	4,593	4,046
27,000	**27,050**	4,054	4,054	4,607	4,054
27,050	27,100	4,064	4,061	4,621	4,061
27,100	27,150	4,078	4,069	4,634	4,069
27,150	27,200	4,092	4,076	4,648	4,076
27,200	27,250	4,106	4,084	4,662	4,084
27,250	27,300	4,119	4,091	4,676	4,091
27,300	27,350	4,133	4,099	4,689	4,099
27,350	27,400	4,147	4,106	4,703	4,106
27,400	27,450	4,161	4,114	4,717	4,114
27,450	27,500	4,174	4,121	4,731	4,121
27,500	27,550	4,188	4,129	4,744	4,129
27,550	27,600	4,202	4,136	4,758	4,136
27,600	27,650	4,216	4,144	4,772	4,144
27,650	27,700	4,229	4,151	4,786	4,151
27,700	27,750	4,243	4,159	4,799	4,159
27,750	27,800	4,257	4,166	4,813	4,166
27,800	27,850	4,271	4,174	4,827	4,174
27,850	27,900	4,284	4,181	4,841	4,181
27,900	27,950	4,298	4,189	4,854	4,189
27,950	28,000	4,312	4,196	4,868	4,196
28,000	**28,050**	4,326	4,204	4,882	4,204
28,050	28,100	4,339	4,211	4,896	4,211
28,100	28,150	4,353	4,219	4,909	4,219
28,150	28,200	4,367	4,226	4,923	4,226
28,200	28,250	4,381	4,234	4,937	4,234
28,250	28,300	4,394	4,241	4,951	4,241
28,300	28,350	4,408	4,249	4,964	4,249
28,350	28,400	4,422	4,256	4,978	4,256
28,400	28,450	4,436	4,264	4,992	4,264
28,450	28,500	4,449	4,271	5,006	4,271
28,500	28,550	4,463	4,279	5,019	4,279
28,550	28,600	4,477	4,286	5,033	4,286
28,600	28,650	4,491	4,294	5,047	4,294
28,650	28,700	4,504	4,301	5,061	4,301
28,700	28,750	4,518	4,309	5,074	4,309
28,750	28,800	4,532	4,316	5,088	4,316
28,800	28,850	4,546	4,324	5,102	4,324
28,850	28,900	4,559	4,331	5,116	4,331
28,900	28,950	4,573	4,339	5,129	4,339
28,950	29,000	4,587	4,346	5,143	4,346

29,000 / 30,000 / 31,000

If line 39 (taxable income) is— At least	But less than	And you are— Single	Married filing jointly *	Married filing separately	Head of a household
29,000	**29,050**	4,601	4,354	5,157	4,354
29,050	29,100	4,614	4,361	5,171	4,361
29,100	29,150	4,628	4,369	5,184	4,369
29,150	29,200	4,642	4,376	5,198	4,376
29,200	29,250	4,656	4,384	5,212	4,384
29,250	29,300	4,669	4,391	5,226	4,391
29,300	29,350	4,683	4,399	5,239	4,399
29,350	29,400	4,697	4,406	5,253	4,406
29,400	29,450	4,711	4,414	5,267	4,414
29,450	29,500	4,724	4,421	5,281	4,421
29,500	29,550	4,738	4,429	5,294	4,429
29,550	29,600	4,752	4,436	5,308	4,436
29,600	29,650	4,766	4,444	5,322	4,444
29,650	29,700	4,779	4,451	5,336	4,451
29,700	29,750	4,793	4,459	5,349	4,459
29,750	29,800	4,807	4,466	5,363	4,466
29,800	29,850	4,821	4,474	5,377	4,474
29,850	29,900	4,834	4,481	5,391	4,481
29,900	29,950	4,848	4,489	5,404	4,489
29,950	30,000	4,862	4,496	5,418	4,496
30,000	**30,050**	4,876	4,504	5,432	4,504
30,050	30,100	4,889	4,511	5,446	4,511
30,100	30,150	4,903	4,519	5,459	4,519
30,150	30,200	4,917	4,526	5,473	4,526
30,200	30,250	4,931	4,534	5,487	4,534
30,250	30,300	4,944	4,541	5,501	4,541
30,300	30,350	4,958	4,549	5,514	4,549
30,350	30,400	4,972	4,556	5,528	4,556
30,400	30,450	4,986	4,564	5,542	4,564
30,450	30,500	4,999	4,571	5,556	4,571
30,500	30,550	5,013	4,579	5,569	4,579
30,550	30,600	5,027	4,586	5,583	4,586
30,600	30,650	5,041	4,594	5,597	4,594
30,650	30,700	5,054	4,601	5,611	4,601
30,700	30,750	5,068	4,609	5,624	4,609
30,750	30,800	5,082	4,616	5,638	4,616
30,800	30,850	5,096	4,624	5,652	4,624
30,850	30,900	5,109	4,631	5,666	4,631
30,900	30,950	5,123	4,639	5,679	4,639
30,950	31,000	5,137	4,646	5,693	4,646
31,000	**31,050**	5,151	4,654	5,707	4,654
31,050	31,100	5,164	4,661	5,721	4,661
31,100	31,150	5,178	4,669	5,734	4,669
31,150	31,200	5,192	4,676	5,748	4,676
31,200	31,250	5,206	4,684	5,762	4,684
31,250	31,300	5,219	4,691	5,776	4,691
31,300	31,350	5,233	4,699	5,789	4,699
31,350	31,400	5,247	4,706	5,803	4,706
31,400	31,450	5,261	4,714	5,817	4,714
31,450	31,500	5,274	4,721	5,831	4,721
31,500	31,550	5,288	4,729	5,844	4,729
31,550	31,600	5,302	4,736	5,858	4,736
31,600	31,650	5,316	4,744	5,872	4,744
31,650	31,700	5,329	4,751	5,886	4,751
31,700	31,750	5,343	4,759	5,899	4,759
31,750	31,800	5,357	4,766	5,913	4,766
31,800	31,850	5,371	4,774	5,927	4,774
31,850	31,900	5,384	4,781	5,941	4,781
31,900	31,950	5,398	4,789	5,954	4,789
31,950	32,000	5,412	4,796	5,968	4,796

* This column must also be used by a qualifying widow(er).

(Continued on page 63)

Whole Numbers and Money **49**

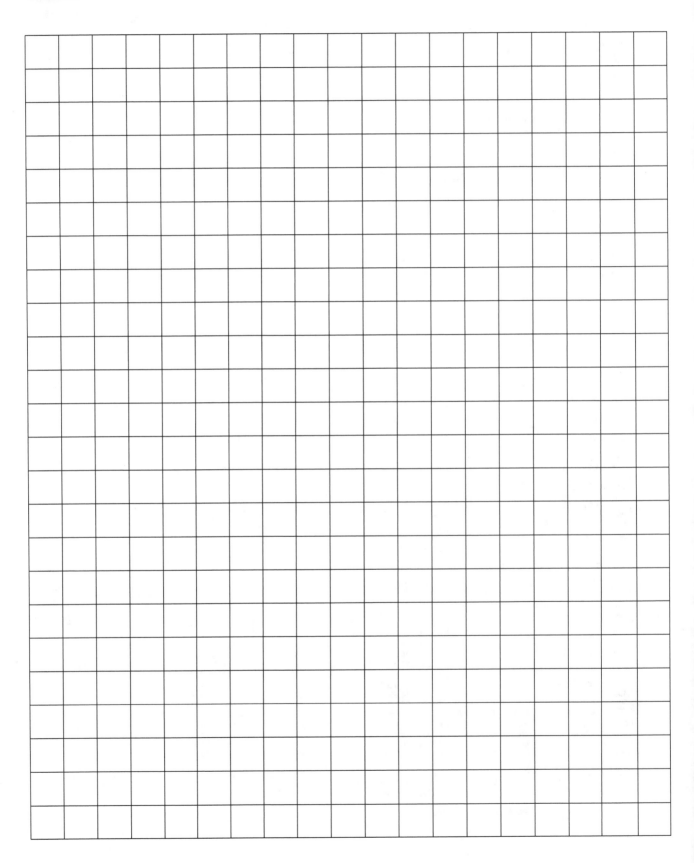

Speed Drill A (one minute)

1	6	1	0	1	5	5	3	3	0
+ 6	+ 3	+ 2	+ 8	+ 7	+ 0	+ 1	+ 4	+ 2	+ 3

3	1	2	3	3	2	4	5	0	0
+ 5	+ 8	+ 5	+ 0	+ 1	+ 4	+ 5	+ 3	+ 5	+ 1

Speed Drill B (one minute)

7	1	3	5	2	0	4	0	4	7
+ 2	+ 5	+ 3	+ 4	+ 6	+ 6	+ 3	+ 4	+ 4	+ 1

6	2	2	2	2	5	4	4	2	0
+ 2	+ 2	+ 3	+ 0	+ 1	+ 2	+ 2	+ 1	+ 7	+ 0

Speed Drill C (one minute)

6	3	9	9	9	4	5	7	6	7
+ 8	+ 9	+ 4	+ 7	+ 6	+ 7	+ 5	+ 7	+ 4	+ 3

6	7	8	3	6	8	5	6	9	8
+ 6	+ 9	+ 4	+ 8	+ 7	+ 7	+ 9	+ 5	+ 0	+8

Speed Drill D (one minute)

9	4	8	2	8	2	9	4	8	4
+ 8	+ 9	+ 2	+ 9	+ 3	+ 8	+ 1	+ 6	+ 9	+ 8

5	7	7	7	3	5	5	7	8	7
+ 6	+ 0	+ 6	+ 8	+ 7	+ 7	+ 8	+ 5	+ 0	+ 4

Adding Large Numbers

- Look at the addition problems below. Some of the answers are not correct. Use estimation to see if the answer makes sense. Circle the problems that have wrong answers.

- Use $1,000, $500, $100, $50, $20, $10, $5, and $1 bills to demonstrate the correct way to do the problems that have wrong answers.

- Show the correct way to do those problems.

- Show how the errors occurred.

	Estimate	Correction	Error
1. $325 + $42 = $367			
2. $51 + $7 = $121			
3. $21 + $463 = $673			
4. $3,101 + $486 = $7,961			
5. $6,421 + $35 = $6,771			
6. $2,143 + $824 = $2,967			
7. $121 + $2,403 + $62 = $9,813			
8. $203 + $41 + $1,005 = $1,249			

Regrouping Chart

Operation ——— Regroup →	Thousands	Hundreds	Tens	Ones

Leonardo da Vinci was an Italian artist who lived during the 15th century. Maybe you have seen the picture below of his "perfect man."

The man in the drawing might be called "a square." Use a ruler to figure out why.

Most people can be classified as

a square ☐   a tall rectangle ▯   a short rectangle ▯

1. With a partner measure your height. It is _____.

2. Then measure your arm span from fingertip to fingertip. It is _____.

3. How would you classify yourself using one of the three classifications listed above? Why?

   _____

   _____

   _____

4. Do you think all people fit into one of these three classifications? Explain.

   _____

   _____

   _____

14 Understanding Word Problems

In each of the following problems, underline the question being asked. Discuss the question to make sure everyone understands what the problem is asking. Use one or more strategies from page 63 to solve the problem. Be ready to explain to the class the problem-solving process you used.

1. One type of scale is a balance scale. You might use a balance scale to weigh potatoes to put in 25-pound bags. You have a container holding 17 pounds of potatoes on one side of the scale. You would put a 25-pound weight on the other side of the scale. You would then fill the container until the scale is balanced. How many more pounds of potatoes do you need to add to the container to make the scale balance?

2. Maria has a special 10-day project to do at work. Her boss says she may decide how she gets paid. Her three choices are

   a. $100 per day for 10 days

   b. $20 the first day, and for the next 9 days, an increase of $20 over each previous day's pay

   c. $5 the first day and double the amount of each previous day's pay for the next 7 days

   Which payment should Maria choose to get the most money? _____

   _____

3. Luis sets up displays for conventions and banquets. He works with square tables that have 3-foot sides. He decorates the tables with table skirts to give them a better appearance. One table uses 12 feet of skirting. When putting tables together, two tables must completely share one side. The shared side does not need skirting. How many feet of skirting does Luis need if he puts together, end-to-end, the number of tables listed below?

   a. 2 tables _____

   b. 3 tables _____

   c. 4 tables _____

   d. 5 tables _____

   e. 6 tables _____

15 | Checking Your Resources

You often have to check to make sure you have enough money to cover expenses. In the following problems, add the costs. (You may want to check your answer with a calculator.) Then write a statement using >, <, or = to explain if you are over, under, or equal to the amount of money needed in the problem.

1. You have $75 in your wallet. You want to buy the pants, shirt, and scarf in the advertisement below. Tax is $5.32.

Shirt	$24.95
Pants	$32.00
Shoes	$44.00
Scarf	$9.50
Cap	$10.95

   Total Expenditure: _____

   Statement: _____

2. You make $472.50 per week. Federal taxes are $70.88, state taxes are $14.18, Social Security taxes are $37.80, rent is $125, and travel expenses are $83. You want to keep $100 in your wallet.

   Total Expenditure: _____

   Statement: _____

3. You have $428.75 in your bank account. The bank requires you keep a minimum of $200 in the account. You want to write a check to make the following purchases: a microwave oven for $149, a set of microwave cookware for $36.95, and a spice rack for $25.85. The tax is $16.95.

   Total Expenditure: _____

   Statement: _____

4. The menu at the Arbor Supper Club has Canadian walleye fillet for $11.95 and an appetizer of onion rings for $2.95. Coffee is 95¢ and cheesecake is $3.75. Tax is $1.57 and tip is $3. You have $23 in your wallet.

   Total Expenditure: _____

   Statement: _____

Cut along the dotted lines.

Name of Item	Name of Item	Name of Item
Regular Price	Regular Price	Regular Price
Sale Price	Sale Price	Sale Price

Name of Item	Name of Item	Name of Item
Regular Price	Regular Price	Regular Price
Sale Price	Sale Price	Sale Price

Name of Item	Name of Item	Name of Item
Regular Price	Regular Price	Regular Price
Sale Price	Sale Price	Sale Price

Subtraction Speed Drills

Speed Drill A (one minute)

9	2	7	6	9	5	4	7	9	3
− 5	− 0	− 1	− 0	− 9	− 1	− 1	− 3	− 7	− 1

3	0	8	7	5	4	8	6	1	5
− 2	− 0	− 3	− 0	− 5	− 3	− 1	− 3	− 0	− 2

Speed Drill B (one minute)

6	6	9	8	8	9	6	9	8	9
− 6	− 5	− 2	− 4	− 7	− 3	− 2	− 1	− 3	− 6

7	4	8	7	6	7	8	4	9	5
− 2	− 2	− 2	− 4	− 4	− 5	− 8	− 0	− 0	− 4

Speed Drill C (one minute)

9	7	8	18	13	14	11	12	15	12
− 8	− 6	− 5	− 0	− 7	− 6	− 8	− 5	− 9	− 8

14	10	16	15	11	13	13	12	10	11
− 7	− 5	− 7	− 8	− 3	− 6	− 5	− 3	− 7	− 7

Speed Drill D (one minute)

11	13	17	11	12	17	14	12	13	11
− 5	− 4	− 9	− 2	− 9	− 8	− 8	− 4	− 9	− 6

15	18	13	11	14	12	16	17	9	15
− 7	− 9	− 8	− 4	− 5	− 7	− 9	− 9	− 5	− 9

Show Your Work

		hundreds	tens	ones
Example: 536 − 32	536 − 32 504	hhhhh 5	~~ttt~~ ~~ttt~~ 0	ooooo~~oo~~ ~~oo~~ 4

		hundreds	tens	ones			hundreds	tens	ones
1.	43 − 23				**4.**	525 − 523			
2.	629 − 615				**5.**	274 − 254			
3.	742 − 542				**6.**	716 − 311			

7. 625 − 5

9. 195 − 105

8. 346 − 36

10. 914 − 812

How would you picture the following problems?

11.   5 feet 7 inches
   − 2 feet 7 inches

12.   3 hours 5 minutes
   − 1 hour

A. Use the regrouping chart to demonstrate the subtraction problems below.

318	5,924	1,673	666	4,214
− 149	− 825	− 746	− 77	− 517

B. Look at the problems below. Can you see any patterns?
If so, test your ideas with problems of your own.

If 35 − 20 = 15, then 35 − 19 = ?

If 74 − 10 = 64, then 74 − 7 = ?

If 56 − 30 = 26, then 56 − 28 = ?

Describe any patterns that you noticed.

_____

_____

_____

C. Use the pattern above to find the answers below. Explain your steps.

45 − 26   64 − 29   82 − 43

D. Look at the problems below. Describe what is happening in each problem.

63	63 + 5 = 68	68	_____
− 35	35 + 5 = 40	− 40	_____
28		28	_____

24	24 + 2 = 26	26	_____
− 18	18 + 2 = 20	− 20	_____
6		6	_____

785	785 + 6 = 791	791	_____
− 694	694 + 6 = 700	− 700	_____
91		91	_____

346	346 + 3 = 349	349 + 50 = 399	399
− 247	247 + 3 = 250	250 + 50 = 300	− 300
99			99

_____

_____

_____

Read the following problems and underline the question in each problem.
Do not solve the problems yet.

1. Mike has a box of copper pennies. He just threw in 36 more to increase his total
to 714 pennies. How many pennies did he have in the box before?

Equation: _____ Answer: _____

2. Dino has decided to use his year-end bonus to buy a $436 TV, a $285 DVD
player, and a $274 TV cart. How much was his bonus if he had nothing left after
he made these purchases?

Equation: _____ Answer: _____

3. As a supervisor, Jesse spends 15 minutes out of every hour checking quality
control. When he finds an error, he hopes to fix it in less than 30 minutes because
he needs time to report his findings within the hour. What is the maximum time
per hour he allows to check for and fix quality control problems?

Equation: _____ Answer: _____

4. Jane had 324 silver dollars. She gave 65 of them to her grandchildren. How many
does she have left?

Equation: _____ Answer: _____

5. Twenty-four days remain before Gina takes her vacation. She began counting the
days right after her last vacation 329 days ago. How many days are there between
one vacation and the next?

Equation: _____ Answer: _____

6. Marguerite had $580 in traveler's checks. That was $85 more than Leslie had.
How much did Leslie have?

Equation: _____ Answer: _____

Working with a partner, write equations for the problems. Use variables to
represent the unknown values. Then solve the equations. Which problems are
similar? How are they similar?

Calories

In general, if you consume 2,500 calories more or less than your normal intake, you will gain or lose one pound.

Calories in Common Foods

Food	Serving Size	Calories
sour cream	1 tbsp.	26
vanilla ice cream	4 oz.	150
American cheese	1 oz.	106
eggs	1	79
ground beef	3 oz.	246
bacon	3 slices	109
chicken, light	3 oz.	142
corn	$\frac{1}{2}$ cup	89
peas	$\frac{1}{2}$ cup	63
potatoes (white)	5 oz.	155
banana	1 medium	104
bread (white)	1 slice	60
hamburger bun	1	120
blueberry muffin	1	190
chocolate chip cookie	1	50
potato chips	1 oz.	150
coffee/tea	8 oz.	0
soda pop	12 oz.	155
beer	12 oz.	146

Listed below are the foods and amounts Martin ate in one day. Use the calorie chart above to fill in the calorie column in the table below.

What Martin Ate	Serving Size	Number of Calories
eggs	2	
bacon	3 slices	
white bread	2 slices	
coffee	8 oz.	
hamburger (ground beef)	3 oz.	
hamburger bun	1	
potato chips	4 oz.	
soda pop	12 oz.	
chicken, light	3 oz.	
corn	$\frac{1}{2}$ cup	
potatoes (white)	5 oz.	
sour cream	2 tbsp.	
vanilla ice cream	4 oz.	
beer	12 oz.	

Answer the questions using the information on PCM 21.

1. Total the number of calories that Martin consumed in one day. If his daily _____
   calorie intake should be 2,500 calories, how many calories below the
   recommended amount is he? _____

2. Assume that Martin also ate the following foods. What would his new total
   calorie intake be?

   1 blueberry muffin _____

   coffee _____

   1 oz. American cheese _____

   4 chocolate chip cookies _____

   1 banana _____

   1 soda pop _____

   $\frac{1}{2}$ cup of peas _____

   Total additional calories _____   **New Total** _____

3. By how much is Martin over a recommended 2,500-calorie intake? _____

4. Use the Exercise Burns Calories chart to choose activities Martin could do to
   burn off his excess calories.

   Exercise Burns Calories!

Activity (1 hour)	Calories Burned
Sitting in a chair	90
Walking	174
Raking leaves	228
Hiking	312
Mowing the lawn	480
Playing tennis	665
Swimming	665
Bike riding	665

   Activities Martin could do to burn off excess calories:

   _____

   _____

   _____

I have 54, who has 4 × 5?	I have 48, who has 9 × 2?
I have 20, who has 5 × 6?	I have 18, who has 2 × 3?
I have 30, who has 6 × 7?	I have 6, who has 8 × 5?
I have 42, who has 7 × 8?	I have 40, who has 4 × 6?
I have 56, who has 8 × 9?	I have 24, who has 6 × 6?
I have 72, who has 9 × 10?	I have 36, who has 7 × 7?
I have 90, who has 10 × 0?	I have 49, who has 7 × 4?
I have 0, who has 1 × 3?	I have 28, who has 3 × 9?
I have 3, who has 3 × 4?	I have 27, who has 7 × 3?
I have 12, who has 4 × 2?	I have 21, who has 8 × 8?
I have 8, who has 2 × 5?	I have 64, who has 4 × 8?
I have 10, who has 5 × 7?	I have 32, who has 4 × 4?
I have 35, who has 7 × 9?	I have 16, who has 1 × 9?
I have 63, who has 6 × 8?	I have 9, who has 6 × 9?

Multiplication Speed Drills

Speed Drill A (one minute)

3	2	4	6	5	4	2	3	0	1
× 3	× 1	× 0	× 2	× 5	× 3	× 4	× 5	× 6	× 9

3	4	7	8	2	6	7	3	0	1
× 9	× 4	× 1	× 0	× 2	× 6	× 2	× 0	× 0	× 1

Speed Drill B (one minute)

1	3	9	2	4	8	5	7	6	7
× 8	× 4	× 5	× 6	× 8	× 5	× 2	× 7	× 3	× 4

2	2	0	8	5	4	8	9	5	8
× 6	× 9	× 7	× 3	× 4	× 6	× 8	× 4	× 3	× 2

Speed Drill C (one minute)

7	6	9	4	8	5	8	9	3	9
× 8	× 4	× 6	× 7	× 6	× 9	× 5	× 3	× 4	× 2

9	6	4	5	6	5	3	7	7	2
× 9	× 7	× 9	× 6	× 8	× 7	× 7	× 9	× 7	× 5

Speed Drill D (one minute)

6	8	6	9	8	6	7	3	5	5
× 7	× 9	× 8	× 7	× 8	× 6	× 4	× 9	× 5	× 9

7	9	7	8	7	8	4	8	0	6
× 9	× 9	× 8	× 9	× 7	× 4	× 9	× 6	× 8	× 2

Understanding Equations

A variable is a symbol that changes value from equation to equation. To solve an equation, find the value of the variable that makes the equation true. For each of the following equations, solve for the variable and write a sentence that explains what the equation means.

1. $n + 18 = 24$

   $n =$ _____ _____

2. $4n = 28$

   $n =$ _____ _____

3. $n - 7 = 18$

   $n =$ _____ _____

4. $6n = 18$

   $n =$ _____ _____

5. $14 - n = 5$

   $n =$ _____ _____

6. $8 + 16 = n$

   $n =$ _____ _____

Discuss the following equations with a partner. How many solutions can you think of for each one? Write a sentence to explain each equation.

7. $a + b = 20$ _____

   _____

8. $ab = 20$ _____

   _____

9. $a - b = 20$ _____

   _____

10. $a + a + a = 0$ _____

    _____

11. $abc = 30$ _____

    _____

12. $y + y + y = 30$ _____

    _____

13. $3y = 30$ _____

    _____

Cut out the dominos below. The dominos can be attached to index cards or cardboard for easier handling.

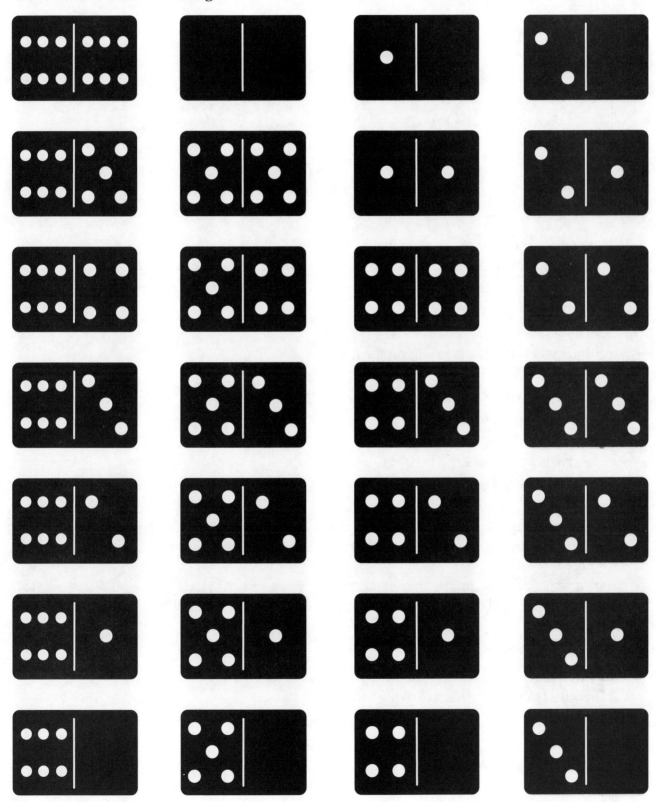

Work in small groups to solve one problem. Then write another question based on the information in your problem. Be prepared to explain your answers.

1. In the Annual Walk-a-Thon, participants collected pledges for the following amounts:

Number of Participants	Pledge per Walker
56	$15
14	$19
33	$20
37	$27
20	$34
10	$68

a. Which two pledge amounts together raised exactly $1,500?

b. Which pledge amount raised the least money?

c. If the 10 pledges for $68 were for $28 instead, how much less money would have been raised?

2. Figure the cost of a resort vacation in the Ozarks using the following information:
   - The seven-day resort package is $1,370 for a family of 4 (meals included).
   - It takes 16 hours, driving 55 miles per hour, and 3 tanks of gas at $26 each to get there.
   - Meals cost about $25 per person per day.
   - Motel rooms run $68 per night for the family.
   - Airfare is $198 per person round-trip.

   a. If you drive 375 miles the first day, how many miles must you drive the second day to get to the Ozarks? Is this a reasonable plan?

   b. Compare the cost of driving a family of 4 to the cost of flying them. What should you consider?

   c. Is it less expensive to stay the 7 days in a motel than at the resort?

3. The shipping log below shows the number of parts received, packed, and shipped per day. Defective items are recorded and returned to the proper department.

Shipping Log

Parts #	Quantity Received	Quantity Packed	Quantity Shipped	Quantity Defective
4206A	35 yards	30 yards	30 yards	5 yards
4207R	376 bags	368 bags	368 bags	8 bags
6431A	96 cases	100 cases	100 cases	0

a. Part #4207R comes in 50-pound bags. What is the total weight of the bags received? shipped? defective?

b. Part #4206A is perforated at 1-inch intervals to break easily into smaller pieces. How many foot-long pieces were shipped? How many 1-inch pieces?

c. A case contains 144 parts and a box contains 24 parts. How many boxes of part #6431A were received? How many parts were packed and shipped?

PCM 28 | Problem Solving with Money

1. You have 2 coins in your pocket. The possible coins are penny, nickel, dime, quarter, half-dollar, and silver dollar.

   a. Make a list of the different amounts that the coins could total.

   b. What is the least amount of money you could have?

   c. What is the largest amount?

2. You have 26¢ in your pocket.

   a. List the different combinations of coins you could have.

   b. Is there a coin you must have?

   c. What is the smallest number of coins you could have?

   d. What is the largest number of coins you could have?

3. You cash a check for $20. List the different combinations of bills you could receive. Explain your answer.

4. You pay a toll of 40¢ twice a day when you drive to work. If you work 5 days a week for 50 weeks a year, how much do you pay in tolls for the year? What are some other expenses you might have if you drive a car to work? List some reasonable expenses. Then figure the yearly cost.

PCM 29 | Billboard Advertising

The Baltimore Bakery has allocated $10,000 for a yearlong billboard advertising campaign. The billboard is 20 feet high and 45 feet long.

The cost of the advertisement includes a string of lights around the billboard at $16.75 per foot. The setup of the advertisement on the billboard is $2.20 per square foot. The rent for the billboard is $365 per month, and the design fee is $1,200.

1. Will any money be left from the $10,000 for other advertising needs? If so, how much?

2. How will the total cost be affected if the billboard is

   a. a rectangle 25 feet high and 60 feet wide?

   b. a square 30 feet on a side?

Keeping Track of Inventory

The warehouse ships five cartons of videotapes. Each carton holds 144 tapes.	A customer returns a shipment of 3,415 videotapes.
The warehouse ships 1,250 videotapes each to ten different customers.	One store buys 15 dozen videotapes. Another buys 850 videotapes. Both orders are sent in the same shipment.
The warehouse ships six crates of tapes. Each crate holds four cartons, and each carton holds 144 videotapes.	The warehouse ships four boxes of videotapes. Two of the boxes hold 450 tapes each. The other two boxes hold 325 videotapes each.
The company manufactures enough videotapes to double the warehouse inventory.	Two trucks deliver a shipment of videotapes to the warehouse. Both trucks hold 28 boxes, and each box holds 15 tapes.
A store sends a truck to pick up three crates of videotapes from the warehouse. Each crate holds 576 videotapes.	A discount store chain returns a shipment of 2,775 videotapes that did not sell after a six-month period.
The warehouse usually ships 3,420 videotapes to All-Star Video each month. This month the warehouse shipped triple the regular order.	The company bundles videotapes, six to a bundle. The warehouse ships 1,500 bundles to a company.
The manufacturer sends five shipments to the warehouse. Each shipment contains 2,500 videotapes.	In the same shipment, the warehouse sends 6 dozen tapes to AA Video, 500 tapes to Video Central, and 4,635 to The Tape Dispenser.

Speed Drill A (one minute)

$0 \div 5 = $ _____ $12 \div 3 = $ _____ $1 \div 1 = $ _____ $21 \div 7 = $ _____ $18 \div 2 = $ _____

$7 \div 1 = $ _____ $15 \div 5 = $ _____ $12 \div 6 = $ _____ $10 \div 2 = $ _____ $14 \div 7 = $ _____

$27 \div 3 = $ _____ $4 \div 2 = $ _____ $0 \div 7 = $ _____ $20 \div 5 = $ _____ $18 \div 6 = $ _____

$9 \div 9 = $ _____ $9 \div 3 = $ _____ $16 \div 4 = $ _____ $6 \div 2 = $ _____ $8 \div 4 = $ _____

Speed Drill B (one minute)

$18 \div 3 = $ _____ $24 \div 8 = $ _____ $32 \div 8 = $ _____ $35 \div 7 = $ _____ $56 \div 8 = $ _____

$36 \div 4 = $ _____ $21 \div 3 = $ _____ $0 \div 6 = $ _____ $40 \div 5 = $ _____ $24 \div 6 = $ _____

$45 \div 5 = $ _____ $27 \div 9 = $ _____ $30 \div 6 = $ _____ $12 \div 2 = $ _____ $49 \div 7 = $ _____

$28 \div 4 = $ _____ $20 \div 4 = $ _____ $8 \div 8 = $ _____ $72 \div 9 = $ _____ $40 \div 8 = $ _____

Speed Drill C (one minute)

$54 \div 9 = $ _____ $16 \div 8 = $ _____ $72 \div 8 = $ _____ $81 \div 9 = $ _____ $36 \div 9 = $ _____

$42 \div 6 = $ _____ $30 \div 5 = $ _____ $48 \div 8 = $ _____ $45 \div 9 = $ _____ $15 \div 3 = $ _____

$35 \div 5 = $ _____ $63 \div 9 = $ _____ $42 \div 7 = $ _____ $24 \div 8 = $ _____ $24 \div 4 = $ _____

$12 \div 4 = $ _____ $56 \div 7 = $ _____ $64 \div 8 = $ _____ $18 \div 9 = $ _____ $16 \div 8 = $ _____

Speed Drill D (one minute)

$81 \div 9 = $ _____ $0 \div 6 = $ _____ $7 \div 1 = $ _____ $18 \div 2 = $ _____ $56 \div 7 = $ _____

$4 \div 4 = $ _____ $21 \div 7 = $ _____ $56 \div 8 = $ _____ $24 \div 4 = $ _____ $15 \div 5 = $ _____

$0 \div 9 = $ _____ $8 \div 4 = $ _____ $48 \div 8 = $ _____ $36 \div 6 = $ _____ $12 \div 3 = $ _____

$32 \div 8 = $ _____ $54 \div 9 = $ _____ $20 \div 4 = $ _____ $72 \div 8 = $ _____ $10 \div 5 = $ _____

Speed Drill E (one minute)

$63 \div 9 = $ _____ $20 \div 5 = $ _____ $40 \div 5 = $ _____ $35 \div 5 = $ _____ $10 \div 2 = $ _____

$30 \div 5 = $ _____ $8 \div 2 = $ _____ $27 \div 3 = $ _____ $49 \div 7 = $ _____ $24 \div 8 = $ _____

$72 \div 9 = $ _____ $16 \div 2 = $ _____ $4 \div 2 = $ _____ $54 \div 6 = $ _____ $42 \div 6 = $ _____

$7 \div 7 = $ _____ $40 \div 8 = $ _____ $35 \div 7 = $ _____ $25 \div 5 = $ _____ $28 \div 4 = $ _____

0	1	2	3	4	5	6	7	8	9
10	11	12	13	14	15	16	17	18	19
20	21	22	23	24	25	26	27	28	29
30	31	32	33	34	35	36	37	38	39
40	41	42	43	44	45	46	47	48	49
50	51	52	53	54	55	56	57	58	59
60	61	62	63	64	65	66	67	68	69
70	71	72	73	74	75	76	77	78	79
80	81	82	83	84	85	86	87	88	89
90	91	92	93	94	95	96	97	98	99

Estimating Division

Place a number comparison symbol between each pair of division problems to make each sentence true. Use your estimation skills to choose the correct symbols.

Comparison Symbols
= is equal to
< is less than
> is greater than

Example: 234 ÷ 6 _____ 464 ÷ 8
Use compatible numbers to find reasonable estimates.
$$240 \div 6 \underline{\hspace{1cm}} 480 \div 8$$
$$40 \underline{\hspace{0.5cm} < \hspace{0.5cm}} 60$$
So you can estimate that
$$234 \div 6 \underline{\hspace{0.5cm} < \hspace{0.5cm}} 464 \div 8$$

1. 584 ÷ 8 _____ 342 ÷ 6
2. 208 ÷ 4 _____ 416 ÷ 8
3. 960 ÷ 10 _____ 780 ÷ 10
4. 189 ÷ 9 _____ 1,890 ÷ 90
5. 469 ÷ 7 _____ 924 ÷ 3

6. 5,523 ÷ 7 _____ 1,824 ÷ 4
7. 6,240 ÷ 5 _____ 4,227 ÷ 3
8. 3,600 ÷ 100 _____ 360 ÷ 10
9. 3,306 ÷ 57 _____ 1,568 ÷ 49
10. 1,938 ÷ 51 _____ 58,092 ÷ 309

- ✂

Measures of Central Tendency

A. Order the Data

B. Analyze the Data

Find the **range:** high _____ – low _____ = range _____

Find the **mean** (average) _____   Find the **median** (middle) _____

Find the **mode** (most frequent) _____

C. Evaluate the Data

- How are the mean, median, and mode the same?
- How are the mean, median, and mode different?
- Which measure best represents the data?

The Chicago Connection

Use the chart to look up distances and the map for airfares.

City	Miles from Chicago
Atlanta	674
Boston	963
Dallas	917
Denver	996
Detroit	226
Honolulu	4,450
Houston	1,067
Las Vegas	1,772
Los Angeles	2,054
Miami	1,329
Minneapolis	405
New Orleans	912
New York	802
Orlando	1,109
Philadelphia	738
St. Louis	289
San Diego	2,064
San Francisco	2,142
Seattle	2,013
Washington, D.C.	671

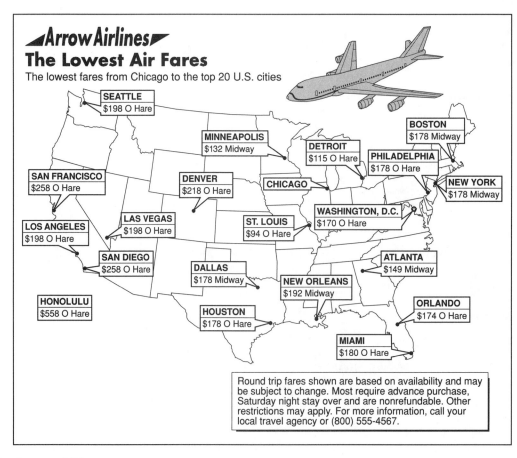

◢Arrow Airlines◣

The Lowest Air Fares

The lowest fares from Chicago to the top 20 U.S. cities

SEATTLE $198 O Hare

MINNEAPOLIS $132 Midway

BOSTON $178 Midway

DETROIT $115 O Hare

PHILADELPHIA $178 O Hare

SAN FRANCISCO $258 O Hare

DENVER $218 O Hare

CHICAGO

NEW YORK $178 Midway

WASHINGTON, D.C. $170 O Hare

LOS ANGELES $198 O Hare

LAS VEGAS $198 O Hare

ST. LOUIS $94 O Hare

SAN DIEGO $258 O Hare

DALLAS $178 Midway

ATLANTA $149 Midway

NEW ORLEANS $192 Midway

ORLANDO $174 O Hare

HONOLULU $558 O Hare

HOUSTON $178 O Hare

MIAMI $180 O Hare

Round trip fares shown are based on availability and may be subject to change. Most require advance purchase, Saturday night stay over and are nonrefundable. Other restrictions may apply. For more information, call your local travel agency or (800) 555-4567.

Deciding What to Do with Remainders

Use your calculator to solve the problems below. Decide what you would do with the remainder, if any. Be sure your answers make sense.

1. How many $16 tickets can you purchase for $75? _____

2. How many 6-packs of soda should you buy so that 115 children each get a can of soda? _____

3. How many dozens of eggs can be shipped from a production of 500 eggs? _____

4. How many trips will it take to carry 50 cubic yards of topsoil if the pickup truck carries 6 cubic yards at a time? _____

5. How many teachers must be hired for a school of 1,255 students if the maximum number of students per class is 26? _____

6. How many boxes of tile at 24 square feet per box do you need to cover the floor of a rectangular room 18 feet by 30 feet? _____

7. How many quart bottles of wine can be filled from a vat containing 11,400 fluid ounces of wine? (1 quart = 32 fluid ounces) _____

8. How many payments will it take to pay off a $3,400 loan if you make a down payment of $750 and pay $86 per payment? _____

9. How many pages long will a book be if there are about 240 words per page and the author has written 15,000 words? _____

10. If you have 900 people to transport, how many buses do you need if the maximum capacity per bus is 78 people? _____

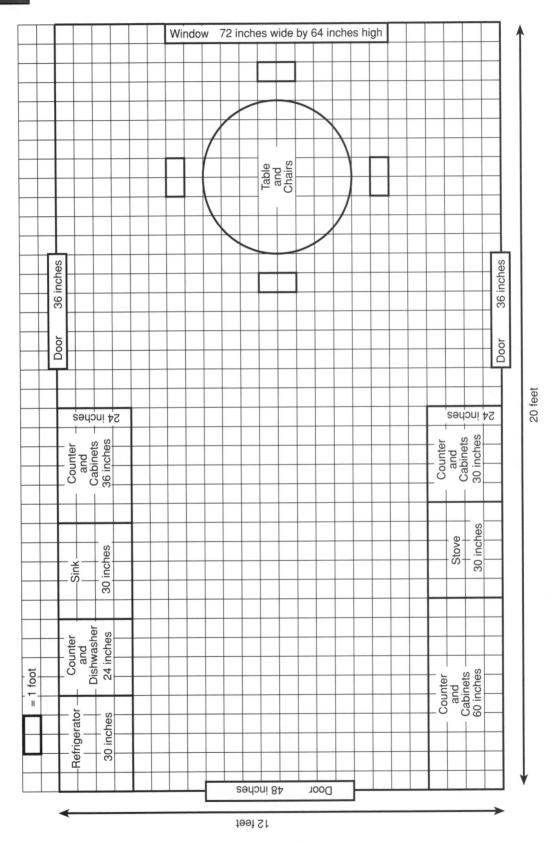

Answer Key

PCM 11: Adding Large Numbers

(Note: Estimates will vary.)

1. Estimate: $330 + $40 = $370

   Correction: not needed

2. Estimate: $50 + $10 = $60

Correction: $51	Error: $51
+ 7	+ 7
$58	$121

3. Estimate: $20 + $460 = $480

Correction: $21	Error: $21
+ 463	+ 463
$484	$673

4. Estimate: $3,100 + $500 = $3,600

Correction: $3,101	Error: $3101
+ 486	+ 486
$3,587	$7,961

5. Estimate: $6,400 + $40 = $6,440

Correction: $6,421	Error: $6,421
+ 35	+ 35
$6,456	$6,771

6. Estimate: $2,100 + $800 = $2,900

   Correction: not needed

7. Estimate: $100 + $2,400 + $60 = $2,560

Correction: $121	Error: $121
2,403	2403
+ 62	+ 62
$2,586	$9,813

8. Estimate: $200 + $40 + $1,000 = $1,240

   Correction: not needed

PCM 14: Understanding Word Problems

1. Possible strategy: write a number sentence

   17 lb. + n = 25 lb. or 25 lb. − 17 lb. = n

   n = 8 lb.

2. Possible strategy: guess and check

   Maria should choose (c).

   Choice (a) would pay $100 × 10 = $1,000.

   Choice (b) would pay $20 + $40 + $60 + $80 + $100 + $120 + $140 + $160 + $180 + $200 = $1,100.

   Choice (c) would pay $5 + $10 + $20 + $40 + $80 + $160 + $320 + $640 = $1,275

3. Possible strategy: draw a picture

   a. 2 tables, 18 ft. of skirting
   (3 + 3 + 3 + 3 + 3 + 3 = 18)

   b. 3 tables, 24 ft. of skirting (18 + 3 + 3 = 24)

   c. 4 tables, 30 ft. of skirting (24 + 3 + 3 = 30)

   d. 5 tables, 36 ft. of skirting (30 + 3 + 3 = 36)

   e. 6 tables, 42 ft. of skirting (36 + 3 + 3 = 42)

PCM 15: Checking Your Resources

1. Total Expenditure: $71.77
   ($66.45 + $5.32 = $71.77)

   Statement: $71.77 < $75

2. Total Expenditure: $430.86
   ($330.86 + $100 = $430.86)

   Statement: $430.86 < $472.50

3. Total Expenditure: $228.75
   ($149 + $36.95 + $25.85 + $16.95 = $228.75)

   Statement: $428.75 − $228.75 = $200.00

4. Total Expenditure: $24.17

   Statement: $24.17 > $23

PCM 18: Show Your Work

1. 20
2. 14
3. 200
4. 2
5. 20
6. 405
7. 620
8. 310
9. 90
10. 102
11. 3 feet
12. 2 hours 5 minutes

PCM 19: Investigating Subtraction

A.
2 10 1	8 11 1	0 16 1	5 15 1	3 11 10 1
3̶1̶8	5,9̶2̶4	1̶,6̶7̶3	6̶6̶6	4̶,2̶1̶4
− 149	− 825	− 746	− 77	− 517
169	5,099	927	589	3,697

B. If 35 − 20 = 15, then 35 − 19 = 16.

   If 74 − 10 = 64, then 74 − 7 = 67.

   If 56 − 30 = 26, then 56 − 28 = 28.

   The answer increases by the same amount by which the number being subtracted decreased.

C. If 45 − 25 = 20, then 45 − 26 = 19.

   If 64 − 30 = 34, then 64 − 29 = 35.

   If 82 − 42 = 40, then 82 − 43 = 39.

D. By making 35 a multiple of 10, regrouping is no longer necessary. Add 5 to 35 and to 63. The new problem is 68 − 40. The answer to both problems is the same: 28.

By making 18 a multiple of 10, no regrouping is necessary. Add 2 to 18 and to 24. The new problem is 26 − 20. The answer to both problems is 6.

By making 694 a multiple of 10, no regrouping is necessary. Add 6 to 694 and to 785. The new problem is 791 − 700. The answer to both problems is 91.

To make 247 a multiple of 10, add 3 to 247 and to 346. The new problem is 349 − 250. Regrouping is still necessary. By adding 50 to 349 and 250, no regrouping is necessary. The new problem is now 399 − 300. The answer to both problems is 99.

PCM 20: Understanding the Question

1. How many pennies did he have in the box before?

   Equation: $714 − 36 = p$

   Answer: $p = 678$

2. How much was his bonus? . . .

   Equation: $\$436 + \$285 + \$274 = b$

   Answer: $b = \$995$

3. What is the maximum time per hour? . . .

   Equation: $15 + 30 = m$

   Answer: $m = 45$

4. How many does she have left?

   Equation: $324 − 65 = s$

   Answer: $s = 259$

5. How many days are there? . . .

   Equation: $24 + 329 = v$

   Answer: $v = 353$

6. How much did Leslie have?

   Equation: $\$580 − \$85 = t$

   Answer: $t = \$495$

PCM 21: Calories

eggs	158	soda pop	155
bacon	109	chicken	142
bread	120	corn	89
coffee	0	potatoes	155
hamburger	246	sour cream	52
bun	120	ice cream	150
potato chips	600	beer	146

PCM 22: Healthy Living

1. $2,500 − 2,242 = 258$

2. $2,242 + 818 = 3,060$

3. 560 calories

4. Answers will vary.

PCM 25: Understanding Equations

1. $n = 6$; The equation asks, "What number added to 18 equals 24?"

2. $n = 7$; The equation asks, "What number multiplied by 4 equals 28?"

3. $n = 25$; The equation asks, "What number less 7 equals 18?"

4. $n = 3$; The equation asks, "What number multiplied by 6 equals 18?"

5. $n = 9$; The equation asks, "14 minus what number equals 5?"

6. $n = 24$; The equation asks, "8 plus 16 equals what number?"

PCM 27: Multiple Solutions

1. a. The group of $15 pledges and $20 pledges reach the $1,500 goal.

      $56 \times \$15 = \$840$ and $33 \times \$20 = \$660$; $\$840 + \$660 = \$1,500$

   b. 14 pledges of $19 each (total of $266)

   c. $400 ($68 − $28 = $40; $40 × 10 = $400)

2. a. 505 miles (16 hr. × 55 m.p.h. = 880 miles, 880 − 375 = 505)

      Answers will vary. It will take more than nine hours to complete the trip on the second day.

   b. Answers will vary. It will take about $800 to fly the family. Gas, food, and lodging for the road trip would cost between $300 and $400. Flying would be easier; you would have more time to spend in the Ozarks. Driving is cheaper, and you get to see the countryside.

   c. Even including the cost of meals ($100 a day for a family of 4), it is cheaper to stay at a motel.

3. a. 18,800 pounds received; 18,400 pounds shipped; 400 pounds defective

   b. 90 foot-long pieces could have been shipped; 1,080 one-inch pieces could have been shipped

   c. 576 boxes were received (144 ÷ 24 = 6 boxes per case; 96 cases × 6 = 576 boxes) 14,400 parts were packed and shipped (144 parts per case × 100 = 14,400)

PCM 28: Problem Solving with Money

1. a. Penny combinations: 2¢, 6¢, 11¢, 26¢, 51¢, $1.01

      Nickel combinations: 10¢, 15¢, 30¢, 55¢, $1.05

      Dime combinations: 20¢, 35¢, 60¢, $1.10

      Quarter combinations: 50¢, 75¢, $1.25

      Half-dollar combinations: $1.00, $1.50

      Silver dollar combination: $2.00

b. 2¢

c. $2.00

2. **a.** 26 pennies; 5 nickels, 1 penny; 4 nickels, 6 pennies; 3 nickels, 11 pennies; 2 nickels, 16 pennies; 1 nickel, 21 pennies

2 dimes, 1 nickel, 1 penny; 2 dimes, 6 pennies; 1 dime, 3 nickels, 1 penny; 1 dime, 2 nickels, 6 pennies; 1 dime, 1 nickel, 11 pennies; 1 dime, 16 pennies; 1 quarter, 1 penny

b. You must have a penny.

c. 2 coins: a penny and a quarter

d. 26 coins: all pennies

3. 20 ones; 4 fives; 3 fives, 5 ones; 2 fives, 10 ones; 2 fives, 1 ten; 1 five, 1 ten, 5 ones; 1 five, 15 ones; 1 twenty; 2 tens; 1 ten, 10 ones

4. $200 ($.40 × 2 × 5 × 50)

Answers will vary. Sample answers are gas, parking, and maintenance.

PCM 29: Billboard Advertising

1. lights (perimeter):
(2 × 20) + (2 × 45) = 40 + 90 = 130 feet

$16.75 × 130 = $2,177.50

set-up (area): 20 × 45 = 900 square feet

$2.20 × 900 = $1,980

rent: $365 × 12 = $4,380

$2,177.50 + $1,980 + $4,380 + $1,200 = $9,737.50

$10,000 − $9,737.50 = $262.50

Yes, $262.50 will be left.

2. **a.** lights (perimeter): (2 × 25) + (2 × 60) = 50 + 120 = 170 feet

$16.75 × 170 = $2,847.50

$2,847.50 − $2,177.50 = $670 more

set-up (area): 25 × 60 = 1,500 square feet

$2.20 × 1,500 = $3,300

$3,300 − $1,980 = $1,320 more

total difference: $670 + $1,320 = $1,990 more

b. lights (perimeter): 4 × 30 = 120 feet

$16.75 × 120 = $2,010

$2,177.50 − $2,010 = $167.50 less

set-up (area): 30 × 30 = 900 square feet (same cost)

total difference: $167.50 less

PCM 33: Estimating Division

1. >
2. =
3. >
4. =
5. <
6. >
7. <
8. =
9. >
10. <

PCM 36: Deciding What to Do with Remainders

1. 4 tickets

$75 ÷ $16 = 4 R11; $11 remainder will not pay for another ticket.

2. 20 six-packs of soda pop

115 ÷ 6 = 19 R1; The remainder shows that 1 child wouldn't get any soda if only 19 six-packs were purchased. The remainder tells you to buy 20 six-packs.

3. 41 dozen eggs can be shipped

500 ÷ 12 = 41 R8; The remaining 8 eggs do not make up a dozen.

4. 9 trips

50 ÷ 6 = 8 R2; One trip would be needed to haul the remaining 2 cubic yards.

5. 49 teachers

1,255 ÷ 26 = 48 R7; 1 teacher would be needed to include the 7 remaining students.

6. 23 boxes of tile

area of floor: 18 × 30 = 540 square feet; 540 ÷ 24 = 22 R12; You would need 1 more than 22 boxes of tile to cover the remaining 12 square feet.

7. 356 quart bottles

11,400 ÷ 32 ounces per quart = 356 R8; The remaining 8 ounces would not fill a quart bottle.

8. 31 payments

$3,400 − $750 = $2,650; $2,650 ÷ $86 = 30 R70; It will take 1 more payment over 30 payments to pay off the remaining $70.

9. 63 pages

15,000 ÷ 240 = 62 R 120; One more page is needed to print the 120 remaining words.

10. 12 buses

900 ÷ 78 = 11 R42; One more bus is needed to transport the remaining 42 people.